Depleted Uranium

Deadly, Dangerous and Indiscriminate

Depleted Uranium

Deadly, Dangerous and Indiscriminate

The Full Picture

first published as
Contribution au débat sur l'uranium appauvri

Principal authors
Anne Gut & Bruno Vitale

Afterword by
André Gsponer

Edited by
Peter Low

SPOKESMAN
for the
Campaign Against Depleted Uranium (CADU)

First English editon published in 2003 by
Spokesman
Russell House, Bulwell Lane
Nottingham
NG6 0BT
Phone 0115 970 8318.   Fax 0115 942 0433.
e-mail elfeuro@compuserve.com
www.spokesmanbooks.com

ISBN 0 85124 685 0

A CIP Catalogue is available from the British Library.

Printed by the Russell Press Ltd (phone 0115 978 45050)

Contents

Acknowledgements

The research and writing of this book was assisted by grants from the Fédération Genevoise de Coopération and the Centrale Sanitaire Suisse (Romande). Numerous friends, colleagues and organisations helped us in exploring the bibliography, finding the key documents, critically analysing the data and arguments, and drafting sections of the text. We wish to thank in particular:
Fermín L. Arraiza Navas (Puerto Rico), the Association of American Lawyers (Karen Parker; San Francisco), José Américo A. Brito (Lisbon), Lorenza Colli, the Comité pro Rescate y Desarrollo de Vieques (Nilda Medina, Robert Rabin; Puerto Rico), Jim Cowan (San Francisco), Felix Dalang, Pierrick Dudognon, Marco Durante (Naples), Hansjörg Eder, Dudley Goodhead (Harwell), the Independent Scientific Research Institute (A. Gsponer, J.-P.Hurni; Geneva), M.J.Haire (Oak Ridge), Gianni Hochkofler, Peter Hug (Bern), Mona Kammas (Baghdad), the Laka Foundation (Henk van der Keur; Amsterdam), Medicina Democratica (Marco Caldirola, Luigi Mara, Bruno Thieme; Milan), Cruz María Nazario-Delgado (Puerto Rico), Domenico Nicco (Naples), Ponte per Belgrado (Fabio Alberti; Rome), Pierre Roussel (Orsay), Margaret Ryle (Sheffield), Monique Sené (Orsay), Hari Sharma (Canada), Stichting Visie (Hans de Jonge; Amsterdam) and Franco Zaccaria (Naples).
We also thank the administration and staff of the United Nations Library (Geneva), who permitted BV to make regular use of their cyberspace.

Note

The major reports about DU which we have quoted frequently in our text may be located easily – in English – through the website of the Centrale Sanitaire Suisse (Romande), thus:

(1) visit the website: www.css-romande.ch
(2) scroll down to 'Depleted Uranium' and click on 'More Information';
(3) scroll down to 'To Download the Main Reference Reports' and click there;
(4) you can then choose the report of the World Health Organisation (as 'WHO 2001'), or the report of Harley et al. (1999, as 'RAND Report'), or the reports of UNEP (2001), ICTY (2001), and the Royal Society (2001 & 2002).

Translators' Note

For some other quotations, the English-language websites consulted for the French edition were no longer accessible at the time of translation into English. In these cases – a small minority – we have 'back-translated' from the French. This method produces the correct meaning, but cannot ensure verbatim accuracy. The translating team, headed by Peter Low, included Negin Almassi, Sally Borrell and Emma Clegg.

Foreword

by the Campaign Against Depleted Uranium (CADU)

There can be no doubt now that the dangers of Depleted Uranium, particularly weapons, have been not only played down but deliberately kept from the general public. Those avoiding the issue include governments, the military and the scientific 'establishment'. This has been made easier by the use of the term 'depleted', which has a reassuring sound, and the often repeated fact that DU is 'only an alpha emitter'. However the chemical toxicity of DU is well documented. The weapons were first used extensively, in 1991, in the Gulf War against Iraq by both the USA and its ally the UK. Although reports began to come in of unexplained illnesses in serving personnel on all sides, and among the civilian population in the south of Iraq, all attempts by sufferers or humanitarian and peace groups to get any recognition by authorities were dismissed.

In October 1998, a group of people in Manchester attended a conference organised by the Fire Brigades Union, on the use of 'Depleted Uranium' munitions in the Gulf War. The audience heard firsthand accounts from Gulf War veterans of their illnesses and their belief that these had been caused by the dust from exploded DU missiles. The group were especially concerned about the information that emerged of the incidence of cancers and leukaemia among the civilian population, particularly children, in the southern area of Iraq, where the DU bombs had been fired. At the same time a letter came to light from the British Ministry of Defence stating that the government saw no problem with DU munitions and that they intended developing the existing anti-tank DU missiles as they were so 'effective'. It was also known that the United Nations Sub-Commission on Human Rights had already declared DU munitions as weapons of 'indiscriminate' effect.

It was decided that a focused campaign was needed and CADU, the Campaign Against Depleted Uranium, was born. CADU aimed to raise awareness of the issues and to provide a centre for the exchange of material on everything to do with the use of 'depleted' uranium.

We know now that the hazards to human health were anticipated in the records of warnings given by the Ministry of Defence to the troops both in the UK and the US. Warnings were not given, however, to civilians of any country where bombing took place, including the

NATO bombings in the Balkans war, since which time much more information has come to light. Scientists had already shown that the DU weapons when fired would leave deadly radiological 'dust' which when ingested or inhaled could lead to cancers and birth abnormalities. On-going scientific research is making the links clearer. CADU has gathered a large body of material and is keen to expand the bank of knowledge. The work carried out for this book, first published in French, not only gathers together existing work, but has new material, including a valuable additional chapter by Professor André Gsponer. This analyses new arguments on the political and military drive behind the development and use of the weapons. We are privileged to be able to publish the work in English and grateful for the cooperation of Spokesman publishing.

CADU wants nothing less than a global ban on the manufacture, export and use of DU munitions.

For further information:
CADU Bridge 5 Mill, 22a Beswick Street, Manchester M4 7HR
Tel: +44 161 273 8293 e-mail info@cadu.org
Web site: http//:www.cadu.org.uk

Introduction

By Peter Low

The view of Tony Blair's government is clearly stated in this reply which Lewis Moonie gave to a questioner:

> Nuclear, biological and chemical weapons are indiscriminate weapons of mass destruction specifically designed to incapacitate or kill large numbers of people. Depleted uranium ammunition is not[1].

If we take those words in their commonly accepted meanings, he was quite right. And the Iraqi Government was wrong to imply the opposite, as they did in the resolution against depleted uranium (DU) which they brought to the U.N. General Assembly in 2002. But that is certainly not the end of the question.

Beyond the polarized 'dialogues of the deaf' which have been common in discussions of this issue, a serious and multifaceted debate has been taking place. It needs to continue, because uranium is not a normal metal, and weapons containing DU are not ordinary conventional weapons – they are radioactive, and this certainly makes a difference. Is it a significant difference? There is real room for debate about this, partly because the adverse effects of low-level radioactivity are slow to emerge. There are also various interpretations of International Law, although the Geneva Conventions certainly require that long-term effects on civilian populations be taken into account. There is also a lot of space for political biases, both for and against DU, which have scarcely assisted the search for truth.

This book argues that DU projectiles are deadly (when striking enemy tanks, for example), and also – more significantly – that they remain dangerous long after impact, because of their radioactivity and their chemical toxicity, and that their effects are indiscriminate. Therefore their manufacture, deployment and use should cease.

The campaign against DU seemed to be new when it arose in the 1990s. Yet in a sense it was just one more task added to humanity's long struggle against barbaric weapons – a struggle that goes back beyond 1945, beyond 1914, as far back as the ancient Romans' debate about *ius in bello* (right conduct of war).

The struggle since 1945 has often focused its efforts on banning the most devastating weapons: nuclear bombs. Those efforts have not succeeded, yet they did increase public knowledge about the dangers of radioactivity, and they seem to have helped the human race to survive past 2000. In the 1990s the struggle even had a few successes, notably international conventions against chemical weapons and landmines. Yet during the same period the overall task actually grew larger, because the scientific-military-industrial complex continues to develop new weapons – such as laser and electromagnetic devices – with no apparent concern for morality and no attempt to publicly debate their necessity or desirability. In today's strange world, one finds the largest military research budgets in the very nation whose military machine already has a huge and undisputed superiority over all others.

The present book focuses on Depleted Uranium, which is doubtless a small part of the world's problems. Yet here we attempt to 'Give the Full Picture', discussing the civilian as well as the military uses of DU, outlining the physical, chemical and medical aspects, and covering many aspects of the debate. One of its underlying questions is: 'Are DU weapons indeed barbaric?' This question needs to be taken seriously and debated in the open, not swept under the carpet as many people seem to wish – including the officials of dozens of nations who voted down a UN resolution calling for a UN-backed study into the effects of DU in Iraq.

Since May 2002, when the original edition of this book appeared in French, the debate has if anything grown in importance. On the one hand the mouthpieces of the military users of DU – notably those of the US Department of Defense and of NATO – have continued to pile up the assertions that it poses minimal risks. On the other hand, the pile of contrary evidence has also grown – notably in reports from Iraq and Bosnia saying that the populations exposed to long-term contamination by DU are suffering increases in various health problems, of which childhood leukaemia is only one. And there are even allegations that radiation from DU has affected the health of workers in the civil aviation industry in Britain[2].

Let us focus on Southern Iraq, the region where DU weapons were first used in battle. The people responsible for the spreading of 400 tonnes of DU there in 1991 were conducting a very peculiar sort of experiment – one in which the 'guinea-pigs' were the soldiers and civilians present … and in which the 'experimenters' did not want to know the results. If we do have good knowledge, now, about the health problems of the Western veterans of 1991, it is only because these guinea-pigs were able to make their squeals heard. But they are not typical of the contaminated population, mainly being exposed for a few weeks at most.

If the 'experimenters' had really wanted to know the results, they could have established proper epidemiological studies in the Basra region, with the cooperation of the Iraqi authorities. It is easy to guess their reasons for not doing so. Such studies would have documented the impact on health caused by the US-driven sanctions. They would have highlighted the malnutrition, water pollution, poor sanitation and barriers to medical supplies (problems which UNICEF and NGOs have long been reporting), and may have mentioned that a ban on importing airborne radiation sensing equipment has prevented the Iraqis from properly monitoring the spread of DU dust. But there is worse: such studies might have disproved the Western claims that DU contamination poses minimal risks. The evidence might even have led to the contrary view – expressed by Helen Caldicott in 2002 – that the very governments most strident in condemning Iraq's terrible weapons have already subjected the Iraqi population to a kind of nuclear war.

Dr. Caldicott gains her information from people like the paediatrician Dr. Janan Ghalib Hassan, who quotes significant increases in a range of malignant diseases, notably childhood leukaemia, lymphoma and neuroblastoma, and whose statistics for congenital malformations rise steeply in the period 1997-2001 from below 4 to over 22 cases per 1000 births. If these figures are accurate, then surely radiation is the main contributing cause. Perhaps we should introduce the term 'downstream damage' for any form of 'collateral damage' that occurs years later (i.e. downstream in time). One kind of birth defect that has risen drastically since 1991 is anophthalmos – congenital absence of one or both eyes[3].

Reports such as those prompted Bruno Vitale to speak of 'New Crimes Against Humanity', in his essay reprinted here, which was first written in September 2000. His title may seem alarmist; yet if one accepts that all weapons emitting nuclear radiation are already illegal (see chapter 13 below), then their actual use would be a 'grave breach' of the Geneva Conventions and Additional Protocols, and therefore legally be a 'crime against humanity'. Besides, in a loose sense, every poisoning of the environment is a crime, and people in every country are part of humanity.

Yet Vitale and his colleagues acknowledge that the questions are not all answered. Hence the central part of this book comprises 'open-ended chapters', exploring the imperfect knowledge available about

DU matters, as part of a debate which needs to continue. For example, chapter 4 highlights the use of DU in the civil aviation industry and chapter 12 draws attention to the Caribbean island of Vieques, where the safety of people near a weapons-testing site seems to have been neglected.

Since these issues remain 'open-ended', let us mention here some recent sources of information that were not included in the French edition:

– A very detailed analysis of DU weaponry has been made by Dai Williams. This is relevant to chapter 3. (www.eoslifework.co.uk/u232.htm).

– A study of DU use in the U.K. has appeared, with particularly useful information about disposal issues. This is relevant to chapter 4. (www.environment-agency.gov.uk/science/242505)

– Regarding the plane crash at Remschied, mentioned below in chapter 7, a new report from the Öko-Institut, Darmstadt, seems to exclude the presence of DU. (www.xs4all/nl/stgvisie/visie/ud_main.html)

– A detailed environmental assessment of depleted uranium has been published by the 'Military Toxics Project'. This is relevant to chapter 8. (www.miltoxproj.org/assesment.htm)

– The 62nd bulletin of the Pandora Project gives details of radioactivity in Bosnia, including news about Hadzici, the area mentioned below in chapter 10. (www.pandoraproject.org)

– The presence of DU in Yugoslavia and Kosovo continues to be documented. (http://members.tripod.com/DUinYU/)

– A recent list of testing sites for DU munitions gives a total of 22 sites

– 13 in the USA, 3 in the UK, and one each in Puerto Rico, Korea, Okinawa, Pakistan, France and Germany. This is relevant to chapter 12. (www.pandoraproject.org/pages/military.htm)

As for the possible use of DU weapons in Afghanistan in 2001-2002, this was not mentioned in the French edition; and we have chosen not to add a chapter here. It is a whole new corner of the debate, and one in which reports and allegations are so far more numerous than reliable data. Two men who are convinced of the presence of uranium contamination are Dai Williams and Dr Asaf Durakovic – who suggest that some or part of this contamination may come from non-depleted uranium[4].

Part III of this book, 'Depleted Uranium Weapons: the whys and wherefores', is as 'open-ended' as the chapters before it. Specially written in 2003 for this English edition, it tries to probe the thinking which produced the original decisions to develop military and non-military products containing DU. It suggests that these decisions are scarcely understandable unless we assume the presence of something quite sinister: a deliberate desire to destigmatise and trivialise the use of radioactive material, and thus to blur the distinction between nuclear and non-nuclear weapons. This desire meant that, for some military planners, the known radioactivity of DU was no impediment to its use but actually an important advantage. Readers may, of course, reject this but they may then find that an explanation based on human folly and blindness is equally unpleasant. In any event, the use of DU has created an indisputable military and legal precedent, and we can expect people to use this to promote new types of nuclear weapons.

The debate about DU needs to be international, considering evidence from various countries; it needs to be wide-ranging, covering all the aspects of the question, and it needs to be well informed. This book contributes significantly to that debate, for example by summarising the legal questions and by exploring the implications for science policies, the responsibilities of UN organs and the opportunities for action by civil society.

Peter Low, New Zealand, 31 January 2003

For those who wish to pursue these questions further, the internet is a good source of up-to-date information. The most reliable information, however, is generally to be found in libraries and professional journals, such as those shown in the bibliographies and references in this book.

Two other relevant books are:
Metal of dishonor; Depleted uranium – How the Pentagon radiates soldiers and civilians with DU weapons (2nd edition). New York: International Action Center, 2000
C. Busby: *Wings of Death; Nuclear Pollution and Human Health.* Aberystwyth: Green Audit, 1995

And here are some relevant websites:
The Campaign Against Depleted Uranium – www.cadu.org.uk
The International Action Center – www.iacenter.org/
The Military Toxics Project – www.miltoxproj.org/
The National Gulf War Resource Centre
   www.ngwrc.org/Dulink/du_link.htm

The Gulf War Veterans – www.gulfwarvets.com
The Uranium Medical Reasearch Centre – www.umrc.net
World Information Service on Energy – www.antenna.nl/wise
The Laka Foundation has a good online library section on depleted uranium – www.laka.org/
The Centre sanitaire suisse-romande has posted on its site (in English) six major reports about DU – www.css-romande.ch

Endnotes

1. Dr Lewis Moonie MP, Under-Secretary of State for Defence: letter to Dr Kim Howells MP about the legality of Depleted Uranium (DU) weapons. Reference D/US of S/LM 1136/01/M (25 March 2001). Excerpt and commentary available at http://www.russfound.org/Launch/farebrother2.htm
2. Garland 2001 www.du.publica.cz/papers/garland.htm
3. The many unverified claims all suggest that the situation is bad, and most point to DU as the chief culprit. Not untypical is the claim that in Basra there has been a '20-fold increase in all cancers' in the period 1991-2001. That is what doctors there told a BBC journalist on 4 July 2002 (www.telegraph.co.uk.news).
4. Williams – www.eoslifework.co.uk/u232.htm
   Durakovic – www.umrc.net/whatsnew.asp

Part I
New Crimes Against Humanity: the Military Use of Depleted Uranium Weapons

by Bruno Vitale[1]

International Politics

> Some young 'veterans' (20 to 27 years old) coming back from war became aware that they had been made to participate in a slaughter and that through conditioning they had been dehumanized and given the status of criminal 'Terminators'. They now understand that the Vietnam war will never have its International Criminal Tribunal; and that the political and military leaders who ordered the massacres, the spread of napalm, the aerial bombing of civilian populations, the massive executions in the prisons, and the ecological disasters provoked by the massive use of defoliants will never be judged by a Court Martial and will never be sentenced for crimes against humanity[2].

Those words, written by Ignacio Ramonet, the director of *Le Monde Diplomatique*, appeared in a recent paper discussing the Vietnam war and 'the exceptional cruelty of a struggle that led to the death of 58,000 Americans and of more than 3 million Vietnamese'.

But that horror story of thirty years ago is being repeated. There will be no International Criminal Tribunal for the new crimes against humanity perpetrated by the political and military leaders of the United States (with the complicity of their British allies) who used weapons containing depleted uranium (DU) against Iraq (1991) and the Federal Republic of Yugoslavia (1999). In fact, when a committee established by the Office of the Prosecutor (OTP) of the International Criminal Tribunal on Yugoslavia (ICTY) reviewed the NATO bombing campaign against the Federal Republic of Yugoslavia, its final report stated that:

> In view of the uncertain state of development of the legal standards governing this area, it should be emphasized that the use of depleted uranium or other potentially hazardous substance by any adversary in conflicts within the former Yugoslavia since 1991 has not formed the basis of any charge laid by the Prosecutor ... It is therefore the opinion of the committee, based on information available at present, that the OTP should not commence an investigation into the use of depleted Uranium projectiles by NATO[3].

17

It seems futile to emphasize the new wave of human and ecological suffering that this new kind of 'potentially hazardous substance' will introduce into modern warfare. The simple use of traditional weapons, be they small arms or standard bombs, is quite capable of destroying human life and of making life in large regions of the world intolerable[4]. But the development of new, more powerful and more efficient weapons by the powers that dominate our world is related to the development of a new, dangerous strategy: 'zero-casualties' warfare, ('zero,' of course, on the side of the aggressor; the number of total military and civilian casualties can increase exponentially) which leaves the vanquished country with its industrial, medical, and educational structures destroyed, its soil and water supplies polluted, and a sick population that no one can take care of, since the so-called 'international community' would impose 'sanctions' following the attack.

Cluster bombs, land-mines, DU weapons... the terror that such an arsenal of horrors can create should suffice to guarantee the control of the world in the 'new world order'. It is in this analytical framework that I wish to develop a few considerations about the burgeoning development of DU weaponry.

We must realise that the development of these new weapons demands a collaborative effort by the political, military, industrial, and scientific establishments; we cannot limit blame or responsibility to only one of these powerful forces in our societies. Strategic imperatives find an enthusiastic response in the dirtiest policies of international power, in the most powerful industrial interests, and in the most ambitious dreams of the scientific community[5]. An active, polemical and efficient opposition to the development and deployment of a new range of weapons should be able to analyse and attack all of these power ingredients together; to reach this aim, we should be equipped with correct, up-to-date information and we should try to go beyond pure denunciation and moral outcry. But how? It is easy to talk, but difficult to find avenues of action.

DU weapons are, of course, only a small part of this strategy of terror. Not all the nuclear states have declared explicit and unambiguous support for the principle of 'no first use'[6]. The massive use of defoliants by the United States during the Vietnam war has never led to any stated policy of abandoning this kind of warfare, notwithstanding the grave, diffuse and permanent damage to people, crops, water, and the whole environment[7].

If we now concentrate on DU weapons, it is not to ignore the grave and global responsibility the major powers bear for forms of terror using other sophisticated means of control and destruction – and it is not merely to protest[8]. Our purpose is to improve our knowledge about a subject that deserves vigilant attention in the future, and at the same time to gain insights into the forces and interests that shape our lives.

One last justification for this kind of reflection: we in the so-called 'industrialised' (or 'democratic') nations live immersed in a cloud of permanent, if hypocritical, references to 'human rights'. Other countries, often with older social systems or tentative new economic structures, are judged by our leaders and moral censors on the basis of the defence of 'human rights'. But these new weapons, inherently disrespectful of human life, human suffering and the long-range destruction of the environment, are 'inhuman wrongs'. If we recognised this, we citizens might react differently to the lies told by our leaders.

I have gathered much of the data discussed below from the sources listed in Table 1. I give the contents of these references in some detail, since the interested reader might find it useful to refer directly to the original sources.

Depleted Uranium and the Development of DU Weaponry
You can find on the Internet a very candid offer of DU manufactured objects. 'Joint-Stock Company Chepetsky Mechanical Plant, Laureate of Government for Quality' presents, on its nicely designed website (http://www.chmz.udm.net/uran_eng.shtml), its 'Depleted Uranium – reliable biological irradiation shielding'. It takes some time to discover that the 'Laureate' refers to an 'Award of the Government of the Russian Federation for Quality' (1998). You can even learn that 'JSC Chepetsky Mechanical Plant had no claims from the customers during all its history' and that it 'is part of the Russian Federation nuclear-power complex'.

What is more surprising is that an 'Application of our depleted uranium by your company will be an important step forward in producing first-rate articles: flaw-detectors, freight containers [!], scientific and medical equipment ... We are ready to produce the required quantity of various depleted uranium articles in the shortest time at purchaser's request'.

This 'civilian' re-conversion of the enormous stocks of DU produced by all nuclear countries as a by-product of the military use of 'weapons grade uranium' and of the nuclear power-plants' use of 'enriched uranium' (see

Tables 2 to 5 for the physical properties of uranium and, in particular, of U-238) is economically comprehensible, but full of dangers. The Chepetsky website does not mention either the extreme chemical toxicity of DU or its weak – but not negligible – radioactivity. As for questions like how to protect workers from these dangers, how to handle these 'first-rate articles', how to dispose of their broken or discarded parts... the Chepetsky website offers not a single word about these.

However, we only have to browse through the Appendices of UNEP/UNCHS (1999) to see that these dangers are very real and reasonably well known:

> As alpha and beta radiation have very limited range in tissue, the dust or particles of DU have to be inhaled or ingested to contribute to the received [radioactive] dose. In the case of skin contamination through contact with solid pieces of DU, there will be some external beta radiation to the skin. ... In short-term toxicity studies it was shown that the kidney is the target organ for uranium [chemical] toxicity (Appendix 4).

The dangers of these civilian applications of DU are minimal, however, when compared with the dangers of the military applications in the production of weapons[9]. The range of DU weaponry already available to NATO countries (US, British and French forces) is large: it goes from the penetrating tips and counterweights of cruise missiles to the DU rounds for the US A-10 Warthog airplanes (used against tanks), the Apache helicopters, the Harrier aircraft, to the 120mm cannon shells used by the US M1A1 Abrams tanks, etc.

The main reason for the development of these applications (apart from the need to deal with the thousands of tons of the very expensive 'nuclear waste' stocked by all nuclear countries) lies in the very high density of DU, together with its extreme hardness when in alloys. These two characteristics make it an ideal component of hard, penetrating projectiles against both armoured tanks and underground military fortifications, and at the same time a very powerful component of the shields of armoured tanks.

The main danger of the military use of DU – to human beings, to the soil and the atmosphere, and in general to the whole ecosystem – is to be found in the chemical properties of DU. Remember that the chemical properties of all isotopes of an element are the same, so that what follows is valid as much for 'natural' uranium as for 'spent' uranium and 'depleted' uranium; but apart from the use of 'weapons grade' uranium in the fission bomb of Hiroshima, the only uranium to which entire populations have recently been exposed is DU.

20

'When a DU bullet impacts on a hard object [such as the armoured plates of a tank or the concrete ceiling of a fortification], it is crushed into fragments and dust. Normally 10 – 35% (maximum of 70%) of the bullet becomes aerosol on impact or when the DU dust catches fire. Most of the dust particles are less than 5 microns in size, and spread according to wind direction. ... If the area attacked consists of rocks and stony soil, most of the DU will be crushed and aerosolized, and thus there will be fallout from DU dust' (UNEP/UNCHS 1999, Appendix 5). 'Uranium that has leaked from fragments and dust particles of DU will be transported in the soil or the bedrock as U^{2+} ions in percolating water. Under oxidizing conditions, most of the dissolved uranium ions are in the form of soluble unaryl ions that can move through the environment and living organisms' (UNEP/UNCHS 1999, Appendix 6).

The nature and the level of risk – to the targeted soldiers who survive the blast and to the civilian population – depend therefore on the chemical form of the DU pollution. When the DU-polluted particles in the aerosol are soluble in water, DU enters the body by ingestion; in this case, the kidneys are the organs that are most easily and rapidly damaged by the chemical toxicity of uranium. When these particles are insoluble, the danger comes from the radioactive dust which is inhaled and deposited in the lungs and can contribute later to the development of lung cancer[10].

Michael Clark, an expert who appears to have very little sympathy with what he calls 'extreme claims' against DU, ('DU is not the extremely lethal danger that some would like to claim it is') states that: 'Any sizeable bare fragment [of DU] has an appreciable contact beta dose rate, typically 2 mSv/h. ... Inhalation or ingestion of DU will incur an enhanced radiation dose internally, but the general scientific/medical consensus is that DU is more of a chemical problem than a radiological one. Ingestion of significant amounts of DU can cause kidney damage due to its chemical toxicity ...'[11].

Those who are responsible for the military deployment of DU weapons have always downplayed both the chemical and the radioactive dangers that it creates for the civil population. It is therefore particularly interesting to read the 'Response Statement' distributed on 15 February, 1999 by the UK Minister of Defence, after a fire broke out in a Royal Ordnance factory handling DU: 'On Monday morning, 8 February, a fire occurred at a Royal Ordnance Speciality Metals factory at Featherstone in Staffordshire. The factory handles depleted uranium and there was initial concern that the fire could have led to the release of radioactivity. The emergency services therefore advised local residents to stay indoors and close their windows'[12]. No warning of the sort was ever given to Iraqi or Serb civilian populations, both amply showered with DU weapons, in the bombing raids!

All the available chemical, physical, and medical information on DU should have made it obvious that the development of DU weapons would be disastrous, and that the inevitable spreading of DU aerosols and dust as a result of their military use would have led to outcomes that can be accurately termed 'crimes of war' and 'crimes against humanity'. Nonetheless, the United States has continued to use it for the last two decades. Concerning the DU weapons projects of the other nuclear powers, we lack detailed information, but we can predict that they are not too different, judging by their industrial-military-scientific complexes! CADU – the UK Campaign Against Depleted Uranium – is 'currently attempting to research manufacture of depleted uranium in the UK'.

The development of DU weapons by the United States started very early. As H. Livingstone writes: 'The use of DU in weapons which can be spread around the test ranges and battlefields of the world is an ingenious solution to the nuclear industry's paralyzing problem of what to do with nuclear waste'[13]. The extent of this 'ingenious solution' can be judged by an official USA document relative to the decommissioning (i.e., closing) of a DU munitions test area at Jefferson Proving Ground, Indiana:

> From 1984 to 1994, the licensee conducted accuracy testing of depleted uranium (DU) tank penetrator rounds at the site ... The DU penetrator rounds vary in size but can be generally described as rods comprised of a DU titanium alloy with a diameter of approximately 2.5 cm and a length as much as 61 cm. The DU munitions testing contaminated approximately 5,100,000 square meters (1260 acres) on the site with an estimated 70,000 kg [70 tonnes!] of DU ... Currently, the licensed material is kept onsite in the restricted area known as 'Depleted Uranium Impact Area'. This area ... is located north of the firing line, and consists of approximately 12,000,000 square meters (3000 acres)[14].

The decommissioning of this test facility does not imply that the development and testing of DU weaponry is stopped or suspended in the United States. In fact:

> The United States Air Force is reconstituting DU air-to-ground training activities at the Nellis Air Force Base in southern Nevada. The Nellis Air Force Base, Nevada, 99th Air Base Wing propose to resume the employment of 30 mm depleted uranium armor piercing incendiary rounds ... This is the only remaining air-to-ground gunnery range in the United States licensed for DU use[15].

So much for developing and testing. The military then had to have their 'ground tests' in a real battle, against real people, and this led to the use of DU ammunitions in both the Gulf War and the NATO bombing campaign against Yugoslavia.

Use of Depleted Uranium Weaponry against Iraq during the Gulf War (1991)

DU weapons were first used openly in the Gulf War. According to the American Gulf War Veterans Association, hundreds of tons of ammunition employing DU were used against Iraqi artillery and armoured vehicles[16]. The veterans estimate that around 600,000 Western coalition troops were exposed to DU in the Gulf.

There is a growing literature concerning the 'Gulf War syndrome' among soldiers of the Western alliance against Iraq, illnesses that are partly blamed on the long-term effects of DU exposure. For instance:

As a result of 'friendly fire' incidents during the Gulf War, the [US] Department of Defense has reported that DU munitions struck a number of Bradley Fighting Vehicles and Abrams tanks [in addition, three Abrams tanks were intentionally destroyed to avoid enemy capture]. The friendly fire incidents killed 13 soldiers and wounded many more. The total number of soldiers wounded by DU is not known; however, the Office of the Army Surgeon General identified 22 soldiers whose medical records indicate they have embedded fragments that might be DU ... Although (the veterans) with embedded fragments have elevated urinary uranium levels, researchers to date do not find adverse health effects that relate to radiation from DU, but several perturbations in biochemical and neuro-psychological testing have been correlated with elevated urinary uranium, the clinical significance of which is unclear[17].

There has not, however, been any serious attempt to study the adverse health effects on the thousands of Iraqi soldiers who were directly exposed to DU bullets (if and when they have survived) and on the millions of Iraqi people who were contaminated – through inhalation and ingestion – by DU aerosols and dust. It is true that the possible negative effects of DU pollution are difficult to separate from the several other health risks that now confront the Iraqi population: industrial pollution from the destruction of oil-wells and refineries, lack of adequate hospital structures, difficulties in obtaining badly-needed drugs because of the embargo imposed by the US and UK, etc. A preliminary report on a 'Child and maternal mortality survey, 1999', produced by UNICEF, – in conjunction with the Iraq Ministry of Health – gives the 'Infant and under-5 mortality rates in Iraq' as growing from 5.4% and 6.7%, respectively, in 1979–1984 to 10.8% and 13.1%, respectively, in 1994–1999[18]. A coordinated set of very intense international projects ought to be launched to estimate the level of DU pollution in Iraq, its possible adverse health effects, and the help needed by the Iraqi population. A few international initiatives have already begun to collect information, as well as urine, blood, tooth, and hair samples from which to test the isotopic content of uranium and therefore the possible presence of DU[19] – while there is a constant intake of 'natural' uranium by our body, and a corresponding metabolic 'biological lifetime' for its elimination, there is no intake of DU from our environment except from DU weapons or from handling DU articles. These projects are clearly not enough. Twelve years have now passed since the Gulf War; the time has come to study in depth the long-term effects of the use of DU on the surviving soldiers and on the civilian population. Careful, well-documented, reliable data could be of crucial importance for a powerful international campaign aiming at the definitive prohibition of DU weapons.

The Use of DU Weaponry on Kosovo and Serbia during the NATO War against the Federal Republic of Yugoslavia (1999)
In a letter dated 7 February, 2000 (almost one year after the beginning of NATO's bombing of Yugoslavia!), the NATO Secretary General George Robertson confirmed to UN Secretary General Kofi Annan that DU weaponry had been used by NATO:

> DU rounds were used whenever the A-10 engaged armour during Operation Allied Force. Therefore, it was used throughout Kosovo during approximately 100 missions. The GAU-8/A API round is designated PGU-13/B and uses a streamlined projectile housing a sub-calibre kinetic energy penetrator machined from DU, a non-critical byproduct of the uranium refining process. The A-10s used DU rounds as part of their standard load. A total of approximately 31,000 rounds of DU ammunition was used in Operation Allied Force. The major focus of these operations was in an area west of the Pec-Dakovica-Prizren highway, in the area surrounding Klina, in the area around Prizren and in an area to the north of a line joining Suva Reka and Urosevac. However, many missions using DU also took place outside these areas. At this moment it is impossible to state accurately every location where DU ammunition was used[20].

News about the use of DU bombs on Yugoslavia (in particular, on Kosovo) was already to be found in the media; in particular, A. Kirby of the BBC published a number of well-documented 'Scientific/Technical' news items on this topic[21]. However, the United Nations Environment

24

Program/United Nations Center for Human Settlements (UNEP/UNCHS), (Habitat) Balkans Task Force, in its preliminary assessment of 'the potential effects on human health and the environment from the possible use of depleted uranium during the 1999 Kosovo conflict' (October 1999, five months after the end of the bombing campaign) was still obliged to state that: '... there are no official documents confirming that depleted uranium was, or was not, used in the Kosovo conflict'. And further: 'The lack of official confirmation from NATO that depleted uranium has, or has not, been used, distorts the prerequisites of this study' (UNEP/UNCHS 1999; see also UNEP 1999 and in particular UNEP/UNCHS 1999a for a more comprehensive analysis of the environmental consequences of the Balkans war).

An official of the UN Task Force therefore had to wait until 7 February, 2000 to be informed about an important aspect of a military offensive that had been launched in March 1999 with the consent of the United Nations (such at least is the folklore knowledge disseminated by the media).

The human and environmental consequences of the use of DU weapons on Yugoslavia are still largely unknown. How much the people of Serbia and Kosovo know about the dangers they incur when handling broken pieces of DU or inhaling dust from sites polluted by DU explosions is unclear. The UK Ministry of Defence is worried, however:

> There are a number of ways in which either UK troops or civilians could be exposed to DU during or after these conflicts. The most likely risk would be if people enter areas that have been damaged and contaminated by DU ammunition ... People visiting or working in Kosovo, for instance press and relief agencies [it seems that Kosovars are not considered significant 'people working in Kosovo'], should seek advice from appropriate authorities on the disposal of damaged vehicles or areas of DU contamination and avoid disturbing these areas. If access to potentially contaminated areas is deemed essential, then advice should be sought from the Ministry of Defence or the Foreign Office on any protective measures required[22].

How far we are from the reassuring tone of the Harley, et al. (1999) RAND report.

Conclusions: Perspectives for Action

The 'concluding remarks and future research' of the RAND report which I have often quoted do not leave room for much optimism:

> In conclusion, the use of DU munitions and armor is likely to expand greatly over the coming years, both in the US military and in other countries. It is therefore important to continue research to further our

25

knowledge of any potential health risks that might result from different levels and pathways of exposure[23].

The scenario looks like this: first you engage in a program to 'expand greatly' your DU weaponry, and then – if and when possible – you engage in a research program to see what its 'health risks' might be!

The Chepetsky offer of 'first-rate (DU) articles', machined from Russian DU arriving from the 'Russian Federation nuclear-power complex', seems to imply that we shall be confronted in the future with a market of civilian goods that will similarly 'expand greatly'. This too will require vigilance and some careful scrutiny. But the great danger is of course the expansion of DU weaponry. Its use in modern warfare reminds us of the very old 'scorched earth' technique used after military victories; and of the symbolic, and perhaps efficient, old technique of covering the enemy's land with salt to make it infertile. The development of DU munitions may have been suggested by the high density and hardness of DU. But it is impossible to avoid the suspicion that the serious consequences of its use – land chemically polluted for years, land radioactively polluted for centuries – may have played a significant role in the strategic choice. Toxic aerosols and radioactive dusts are so much more efficient than salt!

Mere denunciation is of course depressing – we need to do more. DU weapons do not miraculously appear: they are actively researched by scientists, tested by the military, produced by workers in our factories, and used by soldiers in our armies. How can we address the arrogance of scientists in their closed laboratories? How can we address trade unions and workers, who are interested in keeping their jobs, even when these jobs produce napalm, or nuclear weapons, or cluster-bombs, or DU projectiles? How can we address the people around us, and make them aware of what is being prepared for us all?

References

Depleted Uranium Education Project (1997): Depleted Uranium; How the Pentagon radiates soldiers and civilians with DU weapons. New York: IAC, 1997.

GRIP (1999): Proposition de résolution du Parlement européen, visant à interdire l'usage d'armes à u.a., présentée par P. Lannoye, groupe des Verts, June 10, 1999 (www.grip.org).

N.H. Harley, E.C. Foulkes, L.H. Hilborne, A. Hudson and C. Ross Anthony (1999): A Review of the scientific literature as pertains to Gulf War illnesses, vol.7: Depleted Uranium. RAND Corporation, 1999 (www.rand.org/publications) (see Table 1).

M. McGwire (2000): Why did we bomb Belgrade?. International Affairs (U.K.), vol.76, no. 1, January 2000.

Ministry of Defence, U.K (1999): Testing for the presence of depleted uranium in UK veterans of the Gulf conflict; The current position, 24-3-99. (www.mod.uk/policy/gulfwar).

UNEP (1999): UNEP-LED assessment of the environmental impact of the Balkans conflict concludes work in Yugoslavia. UNEP/46 Press Release, September 14, 1999.

UNEP/UNCHS (1999); The potential effects on human health and the environment arising from possible use of depleted uranium during the 1999 Kosovo conflict: A preliminary assessment. United Nations Environment Program/United Nations Center for Human Settlements, (Habitat) Balkans Task Force, October 1999 (balkans.unep.ch; with extensive appendices and a rich bibliography).

UNEP/UNCHS (1999a); The Kosovo conflict: Consequences for the environment and human settlements. United Nations Environment Program/United Nations Center for Human Settlements, (Habitat) Balkans Task Force, October 1999 (balkans.unep.ch).

VISIE (2001): Depleted Uranium Hazard. Holland, 2001 (www.web-light.nl/VISIE/ud_main.html) (see Table 1).

WISE (2000): Uranium project. World Information Service on Energy, 2000 (www.antenna.nl/wise/uranium) (see Table 1).

V.S.Zajic (2000): Review of radioactivity, military use, and health effects of depleted Uranium (members.tripod.com/vzajic) (see Table 1).

Table 1: Main sources
N.H.Harley, E.C.Foulkes, L.H.Hilborne, A.Hudson and C.Ross Anthony (1999): A Review of the scientific literature as pertains to Gulf War illnesses; vol.7: Depleted Uranium. RAND corporation, 1999 (www.rand.org/publications). This is a scientific report whose main aim seems to be to underplay the dangers of the civilian and military uses of DU; nevertheless, it contains quite a lot of useful information and can help in avoiding useless, catastrophic statements; the very fact that it can be taken as a 'hostile witness' gives more weight to its relevant information.
Contents:
  Ch.1: Introduction
  Ch.2: Health effects

Ch.3: Concluding remarks and future research
Appendix A: Principal decay scheme of the Uranium series
Appendix D: Single-particle lung dosimetry
References

VISIE (2001): Depleted Uranium Hazard. Holland, 2001 (www.web-light.nl/VISIE/ud_main.html).
Contents:
Kosovo/Yugoslavia/Netherland/UK
J.Rendon: Concerns about DU
Part of the Executive Summary of an internal UN report about the environmental consequences of the war against Yugoslavia
The effects of using depleted uranium by allied forces on men and the biosphere in selected regions of the southern area of Iraq
Proposed independent study about depleted uranium contamination
DU and other environmental impacts of the Balkans war
Bone accumulation, lung damage; misleading scientific study
Molecular basis for effects of carcinogenic metals on inducible gene expression
J.M.Eaton: Ecological catastrophe and health hazards of the NATO bombing; An annotated URL referenced list of internet articles, news, press releases

WISE (2000): Uranium project. World Information Service on Energy, 2000 (www.antenna.nl/wise/uranium).
Contents:
Introduction
Uranium: its uses and hazards
Uranium radiation and health
Current issues
Uranium radiation properties
Uranium toxicity
Uranium mining and milling
Uranium enrichment and fuel fabrication
Depleted Uranium
Current issues: waste management of depleted uranium
P.Diehl: Depleted Uranium: a by-product of the nuclear chain (Laka Foundation)
Depleted uranium processing and storage facilities
Civilian use of depleted uranium
Current issues

Radiation exposure from dentures containing uranium
Radiation exposure from depleted uranium counterweights
Military use of depleted uranium
Current issues: depleted uranium weapons
H.Livingstone: Depleted uranium weapons
30 mm DU bullet image; GAU-8/A ammunition
L.A.Dietz: Contamination of Persian Gulf War veterans and others
    by depleted uranium
Depleted uranium; A post-war disaster for environment and health
    (Laka Foundation)
D.Fahey: Depleted uranium weapons; Lessons from the 1991 Gulf
    War
R.Bertell: Gulf War veterans and depleted uranium
D.Robicheau: The next testing site for depleted uranium weaponry
R.Bristow: Thoughts of the first British Gulf War Veteran found
    poisoned with depleted uranium
F.Arbuthnot: The health of the Iraqi people
H.van der Keur: Uranium pollution from the Amsterdam 1992
    plane crash
Organisations involved in campaigns against depleted uranium
Radioactive battlefields of the 1990s (The Military Toxics project)
Radiation exposure from depleted uranium weapons
Uranium radiation individual dose calculator
Bibliography: Military use of depleted uranium
Related information sources; depleted uranium

V.S. Zajic (2000): Review of radioactivity, military use, and health
effects of depleted uranium (members.tripod.com/vzajic).
Contents:
Radioactivity
2. Origins
Applications
4. Manufactures
Ammunition testing
Combat and accidents
Radiological effects
8. Chemical toxicity
Gulf War illness
Conclusions
References

Table 2: Data on Natural Uranium
(UNEP/UNCHS (1999), Appendix 4;
www.dne.bnl.gov: Table of nuclides, Uranium;
www.nndc.bnl.gov/htbin/nudat.cgi: Decay radiations;
www.webelements.com: WebElements)

Uranium, element symbol U
Z (atomic number) = 92
A (atomic weight): isotopes known from A = 218 to A = 242;
the isotopes U-234, U-235 and U-238 are found in nature, the
remaining 22 Uranium isotopes are artificially produced

'Natural' Uranium, isotopic composition:

U-234	0.005%	lifetime 250,000 years
U-235	0.720%	700 million years
U-238	99.275%	4.5 billion years

Density: 17 – 19 g/cm^3 (almost double of the density of lead)

Fusion point: > 1130°

Highly toxic, like all heavy metals

Radioactivity of 'natural' uranium: when uranium ore is processed
into 'natural' uranium, the decay products of U-234 and U-235
remain in the waste product. Immediately after 'natural' uranium is
produced, it therefore consists only of the three natural, radioactive
isotopes. After a few months their daughter products will be in
radioactive equilibrium with their parents. The eventual end-
products of all these radioactive processes will be stable isotopes of
lead.

Table 3: Data on Depleted Uranium (DU)
(Diehl, in WISE (2000); UNEP/UNCHS (1999), Appendix 4)

'Depleted' Uranium (DU) is the residual product obtained from the production of uranium fuel ('enriched' uranium, containing in general more than 3.5% of U-235) for nuclear reactors and the preparation of uranium explosive ('weapons grade' uranium) for nuclear bombs.

While large quantities of DU are obtained by the above-mentioned industrial processes, only a very limited amount of it is used in some nuclear reactors; the rest is considered as 'industrial waste'. In some cases, the possibility of 're-enriching' DU has been explored.

Its isotopic composition is:
    U-234   0.0009%
    U-235   0.2%
    U-238   99.8%

However, if DU is produced by the recycling of 'spent' uranium extracted from nuclear reactors, it also contains some plutonium.

Density: 19.07 g/cm³. To achieve better strength and greater resistance to corrosion, molybdenum, titanium or zirconium + tungsten alloys can be used.

Fusion point: 1130°

Highly toxic, like all heavy metals

Fast neutron absorption: better than that of lead

Radioactivity of DU: the decay products of the U-238 present in DU create a series of radioactive elements down to U-234; the decay product of the U-235 present in DU is thorium Th-231; the final fate of all uranium isotopes is some stable isotope of lead. The radioactivity of the different components of DU produces alpha (helium nuclei), beta (electrons), and gamma (electromagnetic) radiation, the last one being only of limited importance.

Table 4: The Radioactivity of DU
The decay chain of U-238

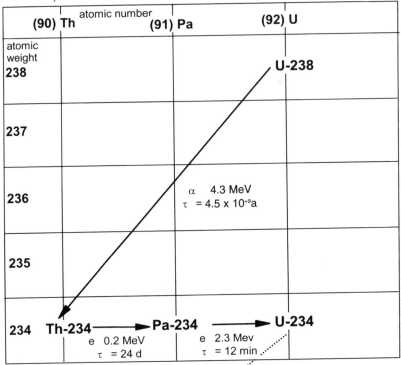

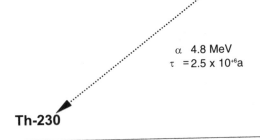

Th-230

---

particles:
    e, negative electron (i.e. a beta particle); α, alpha particle
mean life τ :
    a: year; d: day; min: minute
energy:
    MeV, millions of electron-Volts

Table 5: The Radioactivity of a Dust Particle of DU

Here are a few calculations on the decay of a 'speck' of 1 mg (1/1000 g) of DU (taking account only of U-238):

(with a density of about 20 g/cm^3, this speck has a volume of about 1/20 mm^3, a very small speck that could infiltrate everywhere)

– 238 g of U-238 contains 6×10^{23} molecules (in this case, atoms) of U-238; hence 1 mg of U-238 contains $\sim 3 \times 10^{18}$ atoms.

– The half-life of U-238 is $t = 4.5 \times 10^9$ yr $\sim 1.4 \times 10^{17}$ s.

– Since d $N_t = -k\, N_t\, \mathrm{d}\, t$, so $N_t = N_0 \times e^{-k\, t}$, and $N_t = 0.5 \times N_0$, one obtains
ln $0.5 = -k\, t$, which leads to $k \sim 5 \times 10^{-18}$

Therefore, the number of radioactive decays per second inside a 'speck' of 1 mg of U-238 is of the order of d $N = 1.5 \times 10$ decay/s = 15 becquerels.

(Caution: due to the low energy of the emitted alpha particle, a large part of this radiation will be reabsorbed inside the speck and have no external effects; the radiation emitted will depend on the geometry of the speck: spherical forms favour absorption, while flat forms favour emission)

This represents only the beginning of the radioactive chain which starts with U-238 and results, at the very end, in lead (Pb, stable; see Appendix 4).

It seems to me, therefore, a bit dubious to say that the weak radio-activity of DU renders it harmless: a tiny 'speck' of DU in a tissue or cell bombards the surrounding cells with several particles per second, and continues to do so for a long time until the organism metabolises the foreign body.

Endnotes
1. Physicist; 27, rue des Gares, 1201 Geneva (CH), vitalebrulists@yahoo.co.uk; I am grateful to Jim Cowan for his careful editing of the English text, and to the United Nations Library (Geneva) for my extensive use of their cyber-space.

2. 'Filmer le conflit du Vietnam'. *Le Courrier* (Geneva), 28 April 2000. An earlier version of this essay appeared in English in *Wechselwirkung* (Germany), vol 22, 105/106, Oct-Dec 2000, pp.78-89. I am grateful to Jim Cowan for his editing of that English text. Other versions have appeared in Portuguese, in *Princípios* (Brazil), no. 60, Feb-March 2001, pp. 76-83 and in *Ciência Hoje*, vol. 29, June 2001, pp. 60-63.

3. ICTY (2000): Final report to the Prosecutor by the Committee established to review the NATO bombing campaign against the Federal Republic of Yugoslavia. International Criminal 'Tribunal for the former Republic of Yugoslavia, 2 June, 2000, section A.ii (www.un.org/icty/pressreal/nato061300.htm). The whole document should be considered carefully, as it gives a blanket absolution to all possible crimes committed during the NATO war: '[The committee] has tended to assume that the NATO and NATO countries' press statements are generally reliable and that the explanations have been honestly given ... The committee has not spoken to those involved in directing or carrying out the bombing campaign ... NATO has admitted that mistakes did occur during the bombing campaign; errors of judgement may also have occurred. The selection of certain objectives for attack may be subject to legal debate. On the basis of the information reviewed, however, the committee is of the opinion that neither an in-depth investigation related to the bombing campaign as a whole nor investigations related to specific incidents are justified ... On the basis of the information available, the committee recommends that no investigation be commenced by the OTP in relation to the NATO bombing campaign or incidents occurring during the campaign (Final recommendations).'

4. According to the ICTY – see note (2) – the NATO bombing campaign against Serbia has left at least 495 civilians killed and at least 820 civilians wounded.

5. I tried to develop this analysis, which privileges the paradigm of 'scientific institutions', rather than 'science', in the power interplay of politics/industry/science in capitalistic societies, in three somewhat dated papers: B. Vitale: The neutron bomb. End Papers, no.1, 1981-1982; Scientists as military hustlers. Radical Science Journal (Issues in radical science), no.17, 1985; Military funded research: The institution of science and the military. Current Research on Peace and Violence, 8, 65-73, 1985.

6. See, for instance, the 'NATO Alliance Strategic Concept' (www.state.gov/www/regions/eur/nato), approved by the heads of state and government, 24 April, 1999 (50th Anniversary Washington Summit). No mention of 'no first use' of nuclear weapons will be found in this document; on the contrary, paragraphs 62, 63 and 64 contain the following statements: 'The fundamental purpose of the nuclear forces of the Allies is political: to preserve peace and prevent coercion and any kind of war ...' [...] '... Nuclear forces based in Europe and committed to NATO provide an essential

political and military link between the European and the North American members of the Alliance' [...] '... NATO will maintain, at the minimum level consistent with the prevailing security environment, adequate sub-strategic forces based in Europe which will provide an essential link with strategic nuclear forces, reinforcing the transatlantic link'.

7. During the Vietnam war, more than forty million litres of defoliants were spread over fields and forests; almost 2/3 of this was 'Agent Orange', a mixture of two herbicides (2,4-D and 2,4,5-T), containing dioxin. We note, as a reminder of the powerful industrial interests in modern warfare: Agent Orange was produced mainly by Dow Chemical, Monsanto, and Uniroyal. See in particular: A. Schecter: Agent Orange and the Vietnamese. *American Journal of Public Health*, April 1995. A dramatic, if saddening, photographic exhibition on the long-range health effects of defoliants in Vietnam has been recently touring Switzerland; see the book that accompanies the exhibition: P.Jaeggi (ed.): *Quand mon enfant est né, j'ai ressenti une grande tristesse; Vietnam: Quand les armes chimiques frappent à retardement*. Bâle: Lenos, 2000.

8. But remember the powerful *Protest and Survive* by E.P.Thompson (London: Penguin, 1980), a booklet that played an important role during the European protests against the Cruise and Pershing missiles.

9. Appendix 5 of UNEP/UNCHS (1999) gives precious information on the development of the military use of DU ammunition. See also: Military use of depleted uranium, in WISE (2000) as well as Zajic (2000).

10. See, for instance: Depleted Uranium. Ministry of Defence, UK, July 1999 (www.nrpb.org.uk/D-uran.htm).

11. Michael Clark: Depleted Uranium. Radiological Protection Bulletin, no. 218, December 1999. It should be noted that 'a single day of skin contact with a 2 mSv/h source is equivalent to the maximum dose of radiation acceptable during a whole year', says an expert of the British National Radiological Protection Board quoted by *New Scientist* (1 May 1999). On the other hand, 'a chest X-ray has a radiation dose of about 0.02 mSv' (see Ministry of Defence, UK (1999), p.9, note 22); therefore, a one-hour long skin contact with such a source is equivalent to receiving almost 100 chest X-ray exposures.

12. Ministry of Defence, UK, February 15, 1999 (www.nrpb.org.uk/R2-99.htm)

13. H.Livingstone: Depleted Uranium weapons, in WISE (2000).

14. [US] Federal Register, December 16, 1999; see 'Decommissioning of DU munitions test area at Jefferson Proving Ground (Indiana)', Current issues – Depleted Uranium weapons, in WISE (2000).

15. See 'Resumption of use of DU rounds at Nellis Air Force Range, Nevada', Current issues – Depleted Uranium weapons, in WISE (2000).

16. See www.gulfwarvets.com. Other important sources are: The Military Toxics Project: 'Radioactive battlefields of the 1990s', January 16, 1996, in WISE (2000); J. Shirley: 'Nukes of the Gulf War', 1996

(www.parascope.com/articles); R. Fisk: 'The evidence is there; we caused cancer in the Gulf', *The Independent*, October 16, 1998; US Defense Department: 'Annual report by the Office of the Special Assistant to the Deputy Secretary of Defense for Gulf War illnesses', November 1998 (www.gulflink.osd.mil/library/annual); Ministry of Defence, UK (1999); Harley, et al. (1999); D. Fahey: 'Depleted Uranium weapons; Lessons from the 1991 Gulf War', in WISE (2000).

17. Harley, et al. (1999).
18. 'Child and maternal mortality survey, 1999: Preliminary report'. UNICEF-Iraq Ministry of Health, July 1999.
19. An interesting and growing initiative in this direction is that of the Italian group 'Un ponte per l'Irak' ('Bridge to Iraq'; www.unponteper.eu.org; ponteper@tin.it). A number of NGOs organized on August 18, 1999 – at the UN headquarters in Geneva – a 'Round Table' on the health situation in Iraq, mainly concerned with the presence of DU pollution and its consequences; a document has been published: 'L'assassinat d'un peuple' ('The murder of a people').
20. Quoted in: 'Current issues: Depleted Uranium weapons, Depleted Uranium use in Kosovo', in WISE (2000).
21. Alex Kirby: BBC News, April 9, May 5, June 6, June 7, 1999.
22. 'Depleted Uranium', Ministry of Defence, U.K., July 5, 1999.
23. Harley, et al. (1999).

Part II
'Open-ended' Chapters
Introduction

In his essay about 'How not to make a fool of yourself,' Richard Feynman wrote that 'the idea is to give all of the information to help others to judge the value of your contribution; not just the information that leads to judgement in one particular direction or another' (Feynman 1985). The following chapters keep with this spirit by seeking to broaden and deepen knowledge relevant to the civilian and military uses of DU. Our particular focus will be on the long-term dangers for the environment and entire human populations in regions of conflict exposed to DU.

All of these chapters are necessarily 'open-ended'; they do not reveal absolute truths or give explicit campaign instructions. Instead, they open a forum for mature and well-reasoned reflections that can give each of us, in our personal or group campaigns, effective tools for action. Where possible, we give all the bibliographic details to allow everyone to verify the information presented, consider the arguments, and above all continue to research and analyse.

This task of independent research is unfortunately complicated by the elitist nature of DU literature: almost all of it is found only by exploring the Internet and, on top of that, it is almost always in English. This is unfortunate for those who do not read English, but it would be impossible for most of us to acquire the information of interest in paper form and in other languages, within a reasonable cost and time-frame. So, where possible, we have also listed the e-mail addresses of the referenced people and organisations, so that anyone interested can seek further information that is perhaps beyond the scope of Internet sites.

We think that it is important to begin our exploration with a reasonable measure of scepticism and caution. Obviously, not everything that is in print or on the Internet is true, plausible, or even verifiable. The greatest scepticism is naturally called for when reviewing 'official reports,' which generally come from the structures of information, research, and analysis linked to institutions of power. Similar doses of scepticism and caution should be directed to testimonies and information provided by opponents of DU use – activists who have not necessarily taken the time to verify (or even consider the plausibility of) what they have put forth. We all tend to accept and transmit information that supports what we believe in already, and simultaneously ignore or scorn information that challenges it: an assumption of truth on one side, an assumption of falsity on the other. Through this often subconscious process, a small initial error can translate into a completely mistaken understanding of the situation.

The case for scepticism towards official organisations is strongly supported once we consider the timidity, lack of initiative, and the biased information witnessed in recent years. Some examples (excluding official documents from the United States Department of Defense, the British Ministry of Defence, and NATO) suffice to illustrate this:

(a) Many international organisations, linked more or less to the United Nations or to the United States government, remained silent while DU missiles were being produced, and later used, and while civilian applications of DU were being developed. These include the International Atomic Energy Agency (IAEA), the International Commission on Radiological Protection (ICRP), the United Nations Scientific Committee on the Effects of Atomic Radiation (UNSCEAR), and the Nuclear Regulatory Commission in the United States (NRC).

(b) The World Health Organisation (WHO) entered the debate belatedly, printing a series of publications within a short interval of four months. First came a short official note denying any harmful effects of DU; then a more nuanced report detailing the situation in Kosovo; finally, a long bibliographic analysis of DU which no longer denied its possible negative effects (WHO 2001). Only in recent months has WHO directed attention to the Gulf War, where the first massive use of DU missiles took place.

(c) The United Nations Environmental Programme (UNEP) also ignored the Gulf War in its only publication on DU, which studies the environmental dangers created by the presence of DU in Kosovo (UNEP 2001).

(d) The European Commission chose to make fools of themselves by publishing an 'Opinion of the Group of Experts,' a document denying any dangers associated with DU (EC 2001) without revealing the names of the 'experts.' (I had to resort to press reports to find out that the leader of the group was apparently a certain Ian McAulay from the University of Dublin.) The conclusion stated that 'The experts see no reason to derogate depleted uranium from any provision of the BSS [Basic Safety

Standards], nor to introduce stricter requirements in the BSS for specific uses of DU.'

(e) The AC-Laboratory Spiez, a specialised division of the Swiss Federal Department of Defence, Civil Protection and Sports, put out a nine-page report that mocks opponents and sings the same tune: we have nothing to fear. This is in spite of admitting that 'The problem with the use of DU ammunition probably lies mainly in the fact that after the fighting, in the more highly contaminated places, the remaining local environmental contamination by uranium and its radiation exceeds the internationally recommended standards.' Nevertheless, they claim that 'one cannot directly conclude that there is a health risk for the people living there' (Schmid and Wirz 2000).

(f) The RAND Corporation, a private U.S. research organisation that works primarily on contract for the military, has a slightly different take. In 1999 it completed nine bibliographic studies – financed by the US Department of Defense – concerning the 'Gulf War Illnesses.' (The illnesses and pathologies found among U.S. veterans of the war are generally referred to as 'Gulf War Syndrome.') Each study investigated, separately, a specific 'potential cause' of the 'Gulf War Syndrome'; no effort was made to consider the relationship between one potential cause and another or to consider any possible synergies between them (RAND 1999). (Look, in particular, at their study on DU in Harley et al. 1999.) There have been nine studies undertaken, of which only eight have been published:

Possible effects of infectious illnesses;
The use of 'pyridostigmine bromide' as an antidote against nerve gases that the Iraqis did not use;
(An unpublished study);
Possible effects of stress on veterans;
Possible effects of chemical and biological weapons;
Possible effects of pollution from the burning of oil wells;
Possible effects of the presence of depleted uranium;
Possible effects of insecticide use;
The use of medicines not yet approved by the US Federal Drug Administration.

As a whole, the RAND studies may be useful, but remember that they are – like almost all of the studies mentioned above – only 'bibliographic.' Only an abuse of language and meaning has allowed them to be referred to as 'scientific studies.' The UNEP report is the sole study that provides field data and analysis, which is based on a 15-day visit of experts to Kosovo. Meanwhile, the latest report from WHO concludes with a generic paragraph suggesting 'necessary research' in the future.

(g) Even where these analyses lead to negative assessments of DU, somehow the reports avoid making the logical conclusions. In this vein the Environmental Assessment Division (EAD, which is under the authority of the US Department of Energy) undertook a study dedicated to finding alternatives for using at least part of the enormous DU stocks accumulated by the nuclear powers. Their study led to a rather negative conclusion that 'several regulatory issues might inhibit the likelihood that depleted uranium ... products might actually be produced,' particularly due to 'questions about disposal at the end of a depleted uranium product's life.' But they add that 'DOE might elect to pursue some activities designed to reduce or eliminate regulatory barriers to the production of depleted uranium...products.' They might elect to do so, of course, in order to have a free rein.

The caution we spoke of above should make us clarify and elucidate the best forms of information and action against civilian and military uses of DU. Often, certain alarmist and unverifiable reports become convenient targets for those in power, who make ironic references to them (for example, the aforementioned Spiez report begins by belittling over-dramatic headlines like 'Iraq-Balkans: the Apocalypse Caused by Man!'). One piece of news from early January 2001, which remains unverifiable, reports many hundreds of deadly cancers among the nearly 5000 Bosnian Serb refugees who were forced from the outskirts of Sarajevo to the Bosnian Serb town of Bratunac after the Dayton accords, and links this extraordinary mortality to NATO's use of DU bombs in the Sarajevo 'exclusion zone' in 1995. Should we relay this information? Should we be cautious and seek confirmation? Similarly, we receive worrying information and terrible images from Iraq. Can we attribute all of the malformations found in Iraqi children to DU alone? Do we need to take a more serious epidemiological approach to the situation?

There is good reason to request independent thinking, initiative, and prudence from all readers! The purpose of the following chapters is to provide the instruments that allow for such independence and enable more effective action in the future.

The chapters are in the following order:

1. The Physics of Depleted Uranium and the Chemistry of Uranium (a very simple introduction to the physical properties of DU and the chemical properties of uranium, which builds a foundation for understanding the effects of DU on the human body and the environment)

2. U-236, Plutonium, and Other Transuranic Elements in DU (about the possibility that at least part of the DU used by the military is a product of recycling nuclear fuel)

3. Military Uses of DU (about the different ways in which DU has been incorporated into an array of deadly weapons)

4. Non-military uses of DU (about attempts to normalize and trivialize the presence of DU in everyday objects, without anyone noticing)

5. Metabolisation of DU (about what happens to DU once it enters the human body)

6. Effects of DU on Human Health (about the pathologies that may develop once DU has entered the body)

7. Epidemiology of the Effects of DU on the Human Body (about the 'Gulf War Syndrome,' 'Balkan Syndrome,' the diseases and malformations suffered by people being forced to live in environments contaminated by DU)

8. Effects of DU on the Environment (about how DU behaves once it enters the environment)

9. Iraq (1991) (about the first use of DU, in the Gulf War)

10. Bosnia (1995-1996) (about the use of DU missiles during the NATO air strikes on Bosnia, especially on the outskirts of Sarajevo)

11. Serbia (including Kosovo, 1999) (about the use of DU missiles in Serbia, and particularly Kosovo, during the NATO war)

12. Okinawa, Panama, Vieques, and other United States Military Bases (about the consequences of conducting tests of DU ammunitions on military bases on foreign soil)

13. Laws and International Conventions and the Use of DU (on the body of laws and international conventions that appear to rule that the use of DU is illegal)

Conclusions

Chapter 1

The Physics of Depleted Uranium and the Chemistry of Uranium

The element uranium is a very dense metal with a high melting point (about 1130°C). Its density of approximately 19 g/cm³ is nearly double that of lead and only slightly less than that of tungsten, the densest metal. Uranium is found everywhere in the ground and in water, but almost always in very low concentrations: the average concentration in the earth's crust is about 3 milligrams/kilogram; in the ocean, it is about 0.003 milligrams/litre; and in the human body, it is about 0.001 milligrams/kilogram.

Any chemical element – including, in this case, uranium – can exist in different forms (isotopes). The isotopes of a given element all share the same chemical properties but because of their different atomic masses, each individual isotope exhibits its own physical properties that may differ from the others. Atomic mass is the ratio of the mass of a given isotope's nucleus to the mass of a proton. (Mass number, indicated by A, is the total number of protons and neutrons). The mass of a proton is equivalent to the mass of a hydrogen atom's nucleus (A=1). Thus, given an isotope of uranium with an atomic mass of 238, designated by U-238, its nucleus has a mass approximately 238 times greater than the nucleus of hydrogen.

The uranium found in nature consists of three isotopes: U-234 (relative concentration: 0.005%), U-235 (0.720%), and U-238 (99.275%). However, there are a total of 25 known isotopes of uranium, ranging from A=218 to A=242, all of which are radioactive. Those isotopes not found in nature are artificially produced via radioactive decay of elements with a higher atomic mass than uranium (known as the 'transuranic elements').

U-235 is a necessary component for making one type of atomic bomb (the fission bomb) and central to the functioning of one type of nuclear power station. When U-235 is extracted from natural uranium – the process is known as 'uranium enrichment' – natural uranium becomes depleted uranium, or DU (depleted of U-235). At the end of this process, less than 0.2% of U-235 remains in DU; thus, practically speaking, DU consists of pure U-238 and exhibits all of this isotope's individual physical properties. In some cases, however, DU may be contaminated by transuranic elements (see Chapter 2: U-236, Plutonium, and Other Transuranic Elements in DU). U-238 is radioactive, with a half-life of 4.5 billion years. Half-life is defined as the amount of time it takes for half of a radioactive substance to decay into another element. During radioactive decay U-234 emits an alpha particle with an energy of 4.2 MeV (megaelectron volts); an alpha particle is the nucleus of a helium atom. The resulting element is Th-234 with a half-life of 24.1 days. Th-234, in turn, emits an electron with an energy of 0.2 MeV and decays into protactinium (Pa-234), which has a half-life of 12 minutes. Pa-234 then emits an electron with an energy of 2.3 MeV and decays into another isotope of uranium, U-234. U-234 then decays into another isotope of thorium, and so on and so forth, until the series of decays leads to an isotope of lead, which is stable. All of these radioactive elements can be found in DU several years after its production, contribute to its overall radioactivity, and are said to be in 'radioactive equilibrium' with U-238 and the remaining amounts of U-234 and U-235 in DU.

This series of radioactive decays means that DU possesses 'low-level radioactivity' (about 40% less than the radioactivity of natural uranium) and is referred to as such by the international agencies regulating materials transport. Of the two types of radioactivity emitted by DU, beta radiation (the emission of an electron) is the more dangerous, even though the electrons are rapidly absorbed by the atmosphere. Alpha radiation (the emission of a helium nucleus) penetrates solids and liquids very weakly.

It is difficult to give precise information about the amount of radiation emitted by DU and the threats that this radiation poses to humans. 'Official' documents never fail to emphasise the fact that DU is less radioactive than natural uranium. This may be true, but it misses the point: exposure to DU for a population forced to live in a land bombed by DU munitions is very different from the exposure that miners encounter in uranium mines or factory workers encounter in U-235 enrichment plants.

Calculating the number of ionising particles emitted per second by a given amount of uranium presents one type of problem. Because some of these particles (the alpha particles and the electrons) are absorbed by the interior of the metal, the number of particles emitted per second depends on the shape (the geometry) of a given DU fragment or dust particle. A preliminary approximation ignoring this absorptive phenomenon suggests that a dust particle of 1 mg DU emits roughly 15 alpha particles per second. Supplementary general information on the physical properties of uranium isotopes can be found on the following websites: DUMP (1999), NuDat (2000), UP

(2001), and WebElements (2001); more specific information is provided by EAD (2001).

In contrast to physical properties, chemical properties are the same for all isotopes of an element. Thus it is possible to speak of 'the chemical properties of uranium' without worrying about specific isotopes (WebElements 2001 and EAD 2001 provide good explanations of these chemical properties).

Uranium is a heavy metal, exhibiting many of the chemical properties characteristic of the group of heavy metals in general (mercury, lead, etc.) – particularly their toxicity to humans. When it is in the form of powder or very small fragments, it tends to spontaneously combust upon contact with air at room temperature. Even when in larger fragments or blocks, the metal may swell and crack, and its surface tends to oxidise when exposed to air. When uranium undergoes a violent impact, which results in very high temperatures, it tends to burn in the atmosphere, thereby causing aerosol formation. These aerosols are gaseous suspensions of microscopic particles consisting of different uranium oxides.

One important problem relating to the dangers of uranium's presence in the environment lies in the possible water solubility of its compounds. The aerosols that form upon a collision contain, for the most part, highly toxic but water-insoluble oxides (uranium dioxides and trioxides). This situation applies equally to the case of a DU missile hitting an armoured vehicle or rock, as to the opposite case of a conventional missile hitting a vehicle armoured with DU. Concern about the aerosols created by these types of collisions stems from the subsequent chemical reactions that occur in the soil or in the atmosphere. These reactions generally convert the formerly water-insoluble compounds into equally toxic *water-soluble* compounds: acetates, nitrate, sulfates, etc. Large pieces of DU (left on site after a collision or explosion) tend to react strongly with several substances found in the soil and in water, producing other toxic, water-soluble compounds (see Chapter 8: The Effects of DU on the Environment). The same process occurs when the microscopic particles of aerosols enter the lungs, or when large DU fragments remain in the wounds of soldiers or civilians injured by DU missiles: water inside the human body can lead to reactions turning water-insoluble compounds into soluble ones, thereby promoting DU uptake into body tissue and the kidneys (see Chapters 5 & 6: The Behaviour of Uranium in the Human Body and Effects of DU on Human Health). (See Table 3.2 on the WHO (2001) website for a detailed analysis of the solubility of uranium compounds as a function of the acidity and oxygen concentration of water; see also UNEP 2001, Appendix V: Possible effects of DU on groundwater.)

The way in which DU is generally stored poses another urgent predicament. At the end of the enrichment process (extracting U-235), DU is in the form of uranium hexafluoride, 'depleted UF_6' (DUF_6); these colourless, water-insoluble crystals are radioactive, highly corrosive, and extremely toxic. Furthermore, although solid at normal pressures and temperatures, they can become gaseous at temperatures above 56°C. This is not the best form of DU for long-term storage. These crystals, which are a waste product from the nuclear and military industries, are used to obtain metallic DU for building armoured vehicles, missiles, and possible products for civilian markets.

Given the hundreds of thousands of tonnes of DUF_6 amassed by the nuclear powers over more than 50 years (the United States alone has accumulated over 700,000 tonnes), converting it to metallic DU and finding possible civilian uses for this metallic DU becomes a pressing matter. This urgency is compounded by the problems now facing the United States, where some of the 60,000 steel cylinders storing DUF_6 show signs of surface corrosion. These problems are fuelling a vigorous campaign to find military and civilian outlets for metallic DU (see Chapter 3: Military Uses of DU, and Chapter 4: Civilian Uses of DU). In the words of the Environmental Assessment Division, the challenge is 'to fabricate functional products' (EAD 2001).

The problem is not an easy one. It is becoming painfully clear that the solution of finding 'military uses' for DU presents the fewest obstacles, given how easy it is for military powers to circumvent existing laws and regulations, ignore necessary precautions, and keep at least part of their decisions and projects hidden from the public eye. Despite this the EAD, instructed by the US Department of Energy to find solutions to this problem, drew worrying conclusions regarding the existing legal barriers to using DU: 'existing laws or regulations might create actual or perceived barriers to such use,' not to mention 'questions about disposal at the end of a depleted uranium product's life.' Nevertheless, continues the Environmental Assessment Division report, the 'DOE might elect to pursue some activities designed to reduce or eliminate regulatory barriers to the production of depleted uranium or fluorine products.' Thus, they are not saying that the well-known dangers of radioactivity and toxicity should prohibit industrial use of DU. Instead, they are saying that because of the necessities of uranium storage and military activity, the barriers will have to be modified and the dangers ignored or denied!

Chapter 2

U-236, Plutonium, and Other Transuranic Elements Found in Depleted Unranium

DU, as defined in the first chapter, should contain only U-238 and very small amounts of U-234 and U-235, at least at its time of production. Over time, DU will eventually contain traces of all of the radioactive decay products deriving from the three isotopes found in natural uranium. However, things are not necessarily this simple: shocking, dangerous surprises may be in store.

In August 1999, the US Department of Energy informed the army that the DU armour plating from some army tanks contained traces of technetium (Tc-99) and transuranic elements (those elements that come after uranium in the periodic table). An army laboratory had already conducted a detailed analysis of DU samples, and found the highest concentration for Pu-239, at about 2 parts per million (ppm). They concluded that these other elements were there, but in such low concentrations that they increased by only 1% the radiation to which personnel would otherwise be exposed (Ramachandra 2000). These results were confirmed by NATO (NATO 13 December 2000).

The DU dumped on Iraq during the Gulf War contained U-236 as well, at least in the case of British munitions (3 parts per million; see Hansard 2001). Even though detailed and reliable information on isotopic composition is not yet available, preliminary measurements suggest that certain DU missiles found on the battlefields have much greater surface radioactivity than that predicted for uncontaminated U-238 (Lopez 2001).

A certain number of investigations into the isotopic composition of the DU used in Bosnia and Serbia also appear to confirm the presence of U-236, at a level of 0.0028% (NATO 16 January 2001). In some cases, DU was also found to 'contain trace levels (a few parts per billion) of transuranic elements (neptunium, plutonium, and americium)' (NATO 18 January 2001). However, in its own survey of DU, a German laboratory did not find any plutonium, down to a resolution of 0.0032 parts per billion (ppb) (GSF 2001).

According to a Pentagon spokesperson, Admiral C. Quigley, the presence of 'dirty' DU in DU missiles used in the Balkans was accidental. He says the DU was unfortunately contaminated between the two channels of production (the enrichment process and the recovery process). This event allegedly occurred in the US, at the Gas Diffusion Plant in Paducah, Kentucky, sometime during the Cold War. This 'dirty' DU essentially comes from the residual U-238 recovered from 'spent' nuclear fuel rods after use in nuclear power stations. In the reactor, these rods gradually consume part of their U-235 through fission (the source of energy for nuclear power plants), becoming more and more contaminated by other elements produced during the nuclear reactions. 'Dirty' refers particularly to the artificial elements (elements not found in nature) that have contaminated the rods, which include two other uranium isotopes (U-236 and U-237), the transuranic elements neptunium (Np-237) and plutonium (Pu-239), and the uranium fission products (such as technetium, Tc-99) (WISE-URP 2000).

It is comforting that the DU used for military purposes has low levels of U-236, transuranic elements, and uranium fission products. But the real problem lies in the very presence of these elements in the first place. If DU is the waste from the process of extracting U-235 from uranium – as the US military has always insisted – then DU should only contain U-234, U-235 (whatever amount is left), and U-238. Nothing else. If, on the other hand, the DU used for military purposes (and probably for civilian purposes too) comes from much more suspect and dangerous sources – the reprocessing of nuclear fuel (which gives us good reason to call all DU 'dirty') – then everything we are being told about its possible toxic and radioactive effects could be false and needs to be reconsidered. There are some very serious cases of contamination already known in the United States, in which several tonnes of DU have plutonium concentrations of up to several parts per million (DoE 1985). Unfortunately, the fate of this DU is unknown.

In all of these cases of contamination, the elements concerned are radioactive and generally very toxic. However, it is possible that these elements do not contribute significantly to the dangers that DU presents to the human body. For example, U-236 has a half-life of about 23 million years; it decays into Th-232 by emitting an alpha particle of 4.6 MeV (see Chapter 1 for a definition of the symbols and units used). We can ignore the radioactivity of Th-232 because it has a half-life of 14 billion years. Thus, if U-236 is present in DU at a concentration of approximately 30 parts per million (the highest concentration that has been announced so far), there would be about 3 micrograms of U-236 in one gram of DU, producing about 70 alpha particles per second. Compared to the more than 15,000 alpha particles emitted per second by one gram of uncontaminated DU, this extra radioactivity from U-236 is negligible.

Similarly, the average amount of plutonium contamination – particularly Pu-239 – in dirty DU seems to be approximately 10 parts per billion (Sharma 2001). This translates into a radioactive output of about 20 alpha particles per second for one gram of DU, each particle with an energy of 5.3 MeV (Pu-239 has a half-life of approximately 24,000 years; it decays into U-235). Once again, this contribution is probably insignificant in terms of extra radioactivity.

Nevertheless, trace amounts of plutonium – however minimal – present much greater risks than uncontaminated DU because of plutonium's extreme chemical toxicity. On top of this, dirty DU contains, several years after its production, all of the uranium decay products in radioactive equilibrium with U-238, plus traces of the waste from spent nuclear fuel rods. Thus, the current presence of several toxic and radioactive elements constitutes an uncontrollable cocktail. This makes the decision to dump hundreds of tonnes of DU (whether 'dirty' or not) on vast lands and civilian populations all the more serious.

Chapter 3

The Military Uses of Depleted Uranium

'The US Army began introducing DU ammunition into its stockpiles in 1978, when the United States and the Soviet Union were engaged in intense competition over which side would develop the most effective tank. Washington feared that the Soviets with their T-72 had jumped ahead in the development of armour that was nearly impenetrable by traditional weapons. It was thought that DU rounds could counter the improved Soviet armour' (Mesler 1996). Later, the US army went from the goal of piercing armour plating to constructing impenetrable armour for its own tanks, turning once again to DU. In addition, DU was found to be useful for producing high-penetration missiles and bombs (known as 'penetrators').

It is not useful to give a long and detailed survey of ways in which DU use has developed in the military domain. That would become a very technical discussion on the tactical advantages that these weapons give to combatants, on how the physical and chemical properties were exploited, and on the economic interests that influenced, for example, the choice of DU over tungsten. Such a survey would run the risk, by virtue of its technical nature, of obscuring the political responsibility of military officers, engineers, and scientists who participated in the development of DU, and their responsibility towards civilian populations whose health is being threatened and whose environment is contaminated in the long-term, possibly irreversibly, as a result of military conflict.

With this in mind, this chapter gives information that enables the reader to follow the current debate and to better understand both the extent of military uses of DU in today's armed forces and what, as a result, is at stake.

The chapter offers information only about the presence of DU weapons in the US Army, Navy, and Air Force (see Fahey 1999 for an in-depth presentation, as well as Zajic 1999 and Barrillot 2001). This does not imply, however, that other countries have refrained from acquiring similar weapons; it is simply that the US gives the most comprehensive data, and moreover, as we shall soon see, many of the DU weapons acquired by other countries are US exports.

1. The United States DU Arsenal

Much importance has been given to the role of the US Army's tanks in the Gulf War, the first war in which DU weapons and DU-

49

armoured tanks were used. These were M1 Abrams tanks and Bradley armoured personnel carriers.

For offensive activities, these two types of vehicles have guns firing DU projectiles with diameters of 105mm (M900, with a mass of 3500g) or 120mm (M829, 4500g). These are projectiles specifically created as armour-piercing kinetic-energy penetrators: they do not explode, but fragment and burn through the enemy armour. One of their features is that they are not blunted by impact, but on the contrary are self-sharpening bullets (see WISE 2000 '120mm tank ammunitions'). During the Gulf War they destroyed about 1400 Iraqi tanks.

The A-10 Warthog aircraft of the US Air Force use DU projectiles of 30mm diameter (API PGU 14/B), fired by GAU 8/A guns, which are capable of 65 shots per second in bursts of 2 or 3 seconds. An aluminium cylinder 86mm long and 30mm in diameter covers part of the bullet; inside is a DU cylinder 96mm long and 16mm in diameter (the penetrator) – this is really an alloy of titanium (up to 75% in weight) and DU, with small quantities of iron, nickel, zinc, copper and zirconium (Ristic et al. 1997). This central penetrator has a mass of 292g. (See WISE 2001: GAU 8/A 30mm ammunition).

Other aircraft capable of firing DU bullets are Harrier jets and Apache helicopters (but 'there is no proof that Apaches have ever used them' SIPRI 1999). The F-111s are armed with bombs weighing nearly 2 tonnes each (Guided Bomb Unit 28, GBU-28) for destroying underground defences; they use 'heavy metal' which could be DU (Pike 1998). For other 'penetrators', and specially for DU features developed for Tomahawk missiles, see Jane's 1997 and FAS 2001.

In the US Navy the Phalanx system (an integrated weapons system that protects a warship from attack by surface missiles travelling on the ocean surface), can also use DU projectiles; however, the production of these was stopped in 1988 (SIPRI 1999), and it seems that their penetrators are currently made of tungsten. DU is found also in small munitions: bullets with 7.62mm diameter (unspecified mass); 25mm diameter (200g) and 30mm diameter (380g).

2. The global proliferation of DU weapons

US-developed aircraft and tanks that can use DU weapons, and tanks with DU armour, are now exported to several countries or built there under US licence. Here are figures (SIPRI 1999) for the years 1988-1999:
– M1 Abrams tanks: 561 built in Egypt under US licence; 15 sold to

Egypt, 218 sold to Kuwait and 615 to Saudi Arabia (the export figures for M1 Abrams given by Keur 2000, are much greater, but it is not certain that all the items have DU in their armour).
– Bradley armoured personnel carriers: 400 sold to Saudi Arabia;
– Harrier jets: 18 sold to Italy and 32 to Spain;
– Phalanx systems : 2 sold to Australia, 12 to Brazil, 16 to Canada, 2 to China, 14 to Greece, 8 to Russia, 3 to Israel, 62 to Japan, 10 to Pakistan, 3 to Portugal, 6 to Singapore, 8 to Taiwan, 3 to Thailand, 8 to Turkey and 24 to the UK. (Note that since 1990 the information about Phalanx exports has not been published.)

One must of course add to these numbers the weapons containing DU manufactured by Russia, the UK, France, Pakistan, etc.

In the case of France, a news item from the city of Annecy says: 'For the last fifty years the Nuclear Fuels Industrial Company – Société Industrielle de Combustibles Nucléaires (SICN) – now a subsidiary of Cogéma, has been quietly operating behind protecting walls in the centre of Annecy ... The citizens are unaware that depleted uranium munitions have been manufactured there for use in Leclerc tanks... Evidence of this is the importation in 1993 of 1000 tonnes of [depleted] uranium from the United States' (Jourdan 2001). According to van der Keur 2000, Cogéma is storing nearly 120,000 tonnes of depleted uranium hexafluoride at Bessines-sur-Gartempe, near Limoges.

There are other competitors in the race for DU weapons. One is Pakistan: 'Among the items on display at the IDEX 2001 [Military] Exhibition was the prototype of a new 125mm-diameter bullet with a DU tip designed to pierce tank armour; this bullet is being developed by the Pakistani National Development Complex for use in its T-80UD tanks' (Janes 2001). Pakistan is also busy developing DU weapons for its Phalanx system (Laka 2001).

Israel is often named as another country which probably has DU munitions; however, their possible use in attacks against Palestinians has never been confirmed. In Switzerland, the Defence Department has often 'confirmed that the army does not possess weapons or tanks containing DU materials' (Hug 2000).

POSTSCRIPT 2003: A very detailed analysis of DU weaponry has been made by Dai Williams – www.eoslifework.co.uk/u232.htm

Chapter 4

The Civilian Uses of Depleted Uranium

It is hard to guess what will finally become of the hundreds of thousands of tonnes of DU which the USA (and the other nuclear nations) have accumulated over several decades. A very small fraction has been put to military and civilian uses, and attempts are intensifying to increase these uses and to get rid of the troublesome and dangerous stock. Many civilian uses have been made or proposed; and a certain amount of DU is circulating as a result, with few special precautions being taken. Here, for example, are the quantities of DU compounds (oxides, essentially) exported by the USA alone in 1999 and 2000 (ITA 2001):
– in 1999: 144 tonnes, exported for 2 million dollars (130 tonnes of this went to South Korea);
– in 2000: 84 tonnes, for 3.5 million dollars (including 22 tonnes of DU oxides exported to South Korea and 41 tonnes of other DU compounds to the UK).

There is no bar to the use of DU. For objects weighing over 300g, it is necessary to prove (or just declare?) that the metal will not be reused in a product different from its original use. But recently the US Department of Transport (DoT) made proposals aimed at reducing the international and national barriers to the transport of materials with low-level radioactivity and thus eliminating, in some cases, the need for the materials to be labelled as such while in transit. According to the current norms, the permitted maximum is 70bq/g (70 particles produced by radioactive decay per second per gram); the DoT is asking for this level to be raised, and for there to be no bar to the transport of small quantities (WISE 2001 : « Depleted uranium »).

Numerous warnings have been made about the risks to local populations posed by the presence, the handling and the disposal of DU objects; see for example the analysis of these dangers in WISE 2001, which is a fairly complete overview, and especially the chapters on 'Exposure to radiation from domestic objects containing DU', 'Exposure to radiation from dental products containing DU', 'Exposure to radiation from counterweights made of DU.' See also Mara et al. 2001. Yet in spite of all this, these industrial activities are proceeding apace.

The website of the Manufacturing Sciences Corporation (MSC-USA, an associate of British Nuclear Fuels Ltd., UK) presents the DU products that it can supply. It claims to have produced since 1985 over 70,000 DU objects, 'safe, useful products.' A long list of products follows: radiation protection screens for medical appliances, counterweights for planes ('both civilian and military aircraft'), containers for transporting materials with low-level radioactivity, keels for boats, etc. 'Depending on the depleted uranium application, MSC can also clad the uranium in stainless steel ... for human handling.' As one can see, the MSC does not seem totally ignorant of the dangers of DU. Unlike its Russian equivalent, the Chepetsky State Enterprise (of which more will be said), the website explains that 'MSC performs its depleted uranium operations in a special controlled area that is continuously monitored and where the air is drawn through high-energy filters to remove any airborne dust and particles' (MSC 2001). We are not told, however, about what methods and precautions their customers should use in handling and eventually disposing of the DU objects.

In Russia, however, even that minimum of prudence is not deemed necessary. The website of the 'Chepetsky Mekhanichesky Zavod' tells us their factory has been given an award by the Russian government for the quality of its products, and presents a long list of industrial products made of DU, essentially the same as the MSC's. Given that 'the Enterprise is interested in expanding its activities in Russia and beyond, in order to supply DU machine products, tubes and sheet-metal,' it might be tasteless of us to point out the dangers of DU's double toxicity (chemical and radioactive) and the need to take special precautions in handling and especially in disposing of DU objects. After all, they inform us at the top of the page that 'the radioactivy of uranium can be compared with the level of background radiation emitted by the earth's crust' (Chepetsky 2001).

1. Attempts to make civilian uses of DU more widespread
Uncontrolled activities of this kind have been routine for decades (see Zajic 1999: 'Applications to Aircraft counterweights and DU radiation shielding', WHO 2001: 'Industrial, commercial and military use of uranium'). But pressure to convert DU from the status of 'waste products' to that of 'useful or even essential materials' has increased in recent years. There are clear reasons why this is occurring in the USA, and these same reasons seem to motivate the other nuclear powers.

'The US government has about 500,000 tonnes of DU stockpiled in depots of the Department of Energy (DoE) all over the country. It is generally stocked in the form of depleted uranium hexafluoride (DUF_6) [about 700,000 tonnes] as a result of the enrichment process. The DoE has decided to convert its DUF_6 stock into a chemically more stable form, and has begun a research and development program to study the most effective possibilities for using the recycled DU. This programme will explore the potentially beneficial use of DU' (Price et al. 2001). The cost of the programme – at least for the part entrusted to the national laboratory at Oak Ridge – was $565,000 in 2000 and $1,127,000 in 2001, with $750,000 requested for 2002. Note that in 2001 the DoD allocated in its DU budget an additional sum of $150,000 'for collaborative work with the Russian Academy of Sciences.'

The intense level of international collaboration between the nuclear powers in the field of recycling DU has probably been prompted by the serious problems presented by DU stockpiles (in the form of DUF_6 there are at least a million tonnes worldwide). For the USA alone, there are more than 50,000 steel cylinders each containing 14 tonnes of DUF_6 (some of them over 50 years old), and the stockpiling of DUF_6 continues at a rate of nearly 2000 cylinders per year. DUF_6 is chemically unstable, very active, and corrosive; furthermore, the current state of the oldest cylinders poses problems (Grover et al. 1995). Hence the objective of converting the DUF_6 back into metallic DU or into some of its oxides, and finding outlets for industrial and military products.

Several paths are currently being explored to reach this objective. At a meeting of the 'American Nuclear Society' (the 2000 Winter Meeting, November 2000), there was a debate between researchers from the national laboratory at Oak Ridge and researchers from the Lawrence Laboratory in Berkeley: the former favoured several proposals for recycling the stock of DU for civilian uses; the latter favoured re-using it to extract at least part of the fissile U-235 which it still contains (between 0.2 % and 0.3 %). There was a third proposal, a more radical one, coming from Richard Miller – he favoured 'converting the DU into oxides, conditioning it, and then burying it in abandoned uranium mines' (UEN 2001).

If all the research proposals are followed up, we could well encounter a large number of DU objects in our everyday life, without being warned or conscious of the fact. To give some idea of what may be awaiting us, here are some possibilities:
– The use of certain DU oxides as catalysts for the destruction of volatile organo-chlorate compounds (Hutchings et al. 1996; Dai et

al. 2001; Haire et al. 2001; Price et al. 2001). DU could thus replace cobalt or titanium, which are called 'strategic' materials because they are rare and are found in a very unequal distribution around the different geopolitical regions. As with most proposals for everyday use of DU, there is nowhere any thinking about the eventual fate of the DU after the chemical reaction phase: is it dispersed in the environment and therefore permanently irretrievable?

– The incorporation of DU oxides in matrices made of thermoplastic polymers, so as to make usable, chemically stable, material for radiation-protection screens, counterweights in aircraft, satellite ballast, probes and other equipment for oil prospecting etc (BNL 2000). The only DU applications which seem realistic are those where its nuclear properties are useful: to screen against radiation, to absorb neutrons. But is it worthwhile to use DU (with a relative density of about 19) in places where lead (relative density 11) will do the job? Not in a dental clinic, for example. And let's not forget the problem of disposal after these dangerous objects have served their purpose.

– The incorporation of DU dioxide in a steel matrix (to produce a 'Cermet', a 'ceramic metallic' compound; Forsberg 2001) or in a cement matrix (to produce 'Decrete', which is a 'depleted uranium concrete' compound made by Starmet, under licence from the DoE; Dole et al. 2001). These two products are presented as suitable for the construction of stockpile cylinders for highly radioactive nuclear waste that must be buried permanently or for a very long time. Note that Starmet is a company allied with the aeronautics giant Lockheed Martin, and that it also makes DU counterweights for aircraft. There has so far been no study of the long-term behaviour of these materials under high temperature and humidity (Dole et al. 2001 speak of thermic resistance tests, in water-saturated air, at 66° for a year at most, and at 350° – which might occur in an accident – for 90 minutes). Nor has there been study of the characteristics and nature of their degradation products.

– The use of DU dioxide for making semi-conductors, a proposal arising from some favourable electric properties of uranium oxides (Meek et al. 2001; Price et al. 2001). The stated advantage is that this compound is stable up to temperatures of the order of $2,500^0$, whereas semiconductors based on silicon withstand only 500^0. As far as we can see, nobody except the military could be interested in transistors or microprocessors (or even solar panels) that could operate at over 2000^0. To convert from silicon to DU would require years of research and experiment, in an electronics world totally dominated by silicon; and it is scarcely imaginable that such use could help to reduce the current world stocks of DU.

In all the literature on this subject, one finds no information – or very little – about suggested precautions for the handling and disposal of these DU products, whether those in current civilian use or those promised in future.

The factory processing of DU is already posing problems. One case reported in the British press gives cause for concern. On 8 February, 1999 a fire broke out in an ordnance factory in Featherstone (Staffordshire, UK): '...given that the factory makes, among other things, DU munitions, and given that at first there was anxiety that the fire might cause a radioactive leak, the local emergency services asked all local residents to stay indoors and close their windows'. A radioactive leak did indeed occur, but did not spread 'beyond the building where the fire was' (NRPB 1999).

There is cause for serious concern about the final fate of DU products if they succeed in entering our daily lives. It is well known that uranium oxidises in air, particularly in humid environments, and that any physical or chemical alteration to uranium surfaces can produce serious problems of chemical toxicity and radioactive toxicity when dust is inhaled or ingested. Proposals often suggest the use of a thin coating made of nickel or an alloy of uranium and 8% molybdenum ('non-corrodable uranium'), so as to prevent direct hand contact with these objects and to decrease the risks of oxidation. But what happens when these products are subsequently converted or disposed of?

It is not 'scare mongering' for us to imagine the possible consequences of inappropriate use or disposal of DU products, as with any other toxic or radioactive substances. We can call to mind the Aparecida de Goiânia case, where serious radioactive pollution was caused by the unknown presence of a capsule of caesium (Cs-137) among some metal fragments disposed of in 1987 in a scrap metal dump in the Brazilian state of Goiânia. The capsule came from the radiotherapy equipment of a bankrupted private clinic, part of whose equipment had been dumped. One child died, hundreds of children were contaminated, and a whole region had to be monitored for years (CH 2000). And we can also note a more recent episode, one directly involving DU, where the police in India found 8kg of DU in the possession of a scrap-metal merchant (SO 2000).

2. The aeronautical use of DU and the crash of the El-Al Boeing 747 at Bijlermeer (Amsterdam-Schipol Airport)

The above paragraphs have often mentioned the use of DU counterweights in civilian and military aircraft. These DU weights – ranging from 0.23kg to 77 kg – move about automatically in a plane in order to compensate for the lightening of fuel-tanks or movements in the load, and can replace lead counterweights, which occupy more space per kilogram (tungsten counterweights are also in use at present).

Several aircraft manufacturers put these counterweights into their planes without taking account of the potential risks, at least not at the start. There are risks when they are handled and repaired, and potential dangers of chemical and radioactive pollution if crashes or other accidents occur. The propensity of uranium to ignite, which we mentioned in Chapter 1, means that these counterweights could burst into flame when subject to violent shock and create a cloud of toxic dust (an aerosol) capable of contaminating wide areas – far beyond the site of the accident (see ch. 5 on the behaviour of uranium in the human body and the possible channels of contamination; see also Mara et al. 2001 for a more detailed account).

Boeing, for example, used DU counterweights (between 1968 and 1981) in 551 of its 747s (Laka 2001), and 202 of these aircraft were still in service with commercial airlines in 2001; McDonnell-Douglas has them in 168 of its DC-10s still flying and in some MD-11 aircraft; Lockheed has them in 60 of its L-1011 aircraft still in service (WISE 2001: 'Radiation exposure from depleted uranium counterweights'). And it was a Boeing 747, equipped with 20 counterweights totalling nearly 850kg, that crashed at Lockerbie, Scotland in 1988: 18 counterweights were salvaged, 2 were not found. When the local authorities asked Boeing for information about the dangers linked to the loss of these two counterweights, they were told 'these counterweights had been tested by NASA and are completely safe' (McNeil 1990). A few weeks before the crash, a US physicist had published an article in the science journal *Nature* denouncing the dangers of putting DU into civilian aircraft; according to it, if a 747 crashed and all its DU ignited (the conceivable 'worst-case scenario'), up to 250,000 people would risk poisoning by inhaling or ingesting uranium oxide dust (Parker 1988).

Some years later, on 4 October 1992, a Boeing 747 cargo aircraft belonging to the Israeli airline El Al crashed shortly after take-off onto blocks of flats near Amsterdam's Schipol Airport, in the Bijlermeer neighbourhood. There were 43 deaths (mostly local residents) and extensive damage, because the plane – which burst into flames on impact producing temperatures exceeding 500° – had just refilled its fuel tanks (much detail is available in Uijt de Haa et al. 2000).

It seems likely that this plane had been loaded with several tonnes of highly flammable chemicals used for making toxic gases. In any case, for a long time El Al blocked attempts by the Dutch authorities to identify with certainty all the toxic substances carried on board, by destroying the flight documents concerning 20 tonnes of the cargo. Later the Israeli government admitted that these included the chemical compound DMMP, which can be used to make the neuro-toxic gas Sarin; but alleged that it had been imported from the USA 'for testing filters' (McBride 1999).

It was subsequently revealed that the aircraft had two DU counterweights in the rudder section, totalling 282 kg. The information supplied by Boeing was confusing: they spoke of 435 kg when the plane was built – of which 45 kg of DU was later replaced with tungsten – but finally gave a figure of 282 kg. 90 kg was recovered in the initial salvaging, and an additional 40 kg later. This would leave nearly 150 kg of DU which either dispersed as an aerosol into the environment or remained as small crash fragments in the blocks of flats or in the hangar where the debris was stored. A Dutch commission of inquiry subsequently concluded that at least some of the unrecovered DU was dispersed into the atmosphere as microscopic particles and could have been inhaled by rescue workers and local residents (van der Keur 1999).

The chemical analysis of dust samples taken in the hangar containing the debris (Hangar 8) gives a uranium concentration (all isotopes combined) of 14.4 ppm (parts per million) – compare this concentration with the average concentration in the earth's crust, which is 2.7 ppm. The dust in the hangar therefore contains five times the average amount of uranium, but uranium concentrations vary greatly, and a deviation from the average figure for the earth's crust is not very significant.

On the other hand, an isotopic analysis of the uranium dust collected in the air filters of the housing blocks destroyed by the crash and the fire produced more disturbing results: it seems that the DU present in the plane did not have the same isotopic composition as DU that is produced by the enrichment process (see ch. 1). On the contrary, it had the following isotopic composition: U-234 = 0.0054%, U-235 = 0.6597%, U-236 = 0.0006%, U-238 = 99.3343%

(percentages of the number of atoms: de Jonge 2000). These figures are still provisional and the data can change with more accurate and reliable measurements: but the possible presence of U-236 (which does not exist in nature and is produced only by nuclear power-plants) gives cause for anxiety. One must wonder whether this was 'dirty' DU, DU which is produced in the process of recycling the fuel rods of a power-plant and which contains U-236 and also traces of plutonium and other transuranic elements (for more details see ch.2 'U-236, Plutonium and other transuranic elements').

The problem faced by the Amsterdam region is faced by every place where a major air accident occurs. Since 1972, at least 40 air accidents have caused the total destruction of a Boeing 747, an L-1011 or a DC-10 (Mara et al. 2001), including the accident at Stansted in England (22 December 1999). The facts are unclear, but it is very probable that at least some of these aircraft had DU counterweights.

To conclude: the potential risks of civilian use of DU are such that any spread of this activity, whether research or industrial production, must be defined as dangerous both for the personnel who work, handle or dispose of this material and for the general population. Any attempts to normalise the presence of DU objects in everyday life – in electronic products (transistors), in means of transport (aircraft, boats), in chemical and biological laboratories (as catalysts) etc. – constitute an unacceptable threat to people's health and to the environment. The long-term dangers of low-level radiation are still essentially unknown, but it seems that there is no threshold effect and therefore that any increase above background radiation can produce an increase in human morbidity and mortality. The same applies to the effects of a chemically toxic environment on human immuno-defense mechanisms.

How can we account for the desire of some people to force us to live with DU in our everyday lives? One obvious reason is their wish to get rid of a troublesome, dangerous stockpile, while gaining maximum financial profit.

Note

A more complete and detailed report (in Italian) about the civilian uses of DU and its dangers is Mara et al. 2001. This places the question in the more general context of the chemical and radioactive toxicity of uranium and the political and economic issues surrounding its use. This report may be requested from the authors:

Luigi Mara, Bruno Theme e Marco Caldirola: 'Rischi, malattie e morte da uranio impoverito'. Milano : Medicina Democratica 2001. Medicina Democratica, via Venezian 1 – I-20133 Milano (medicinademocratica@libero.it)

A detailed list of radioactive materials (including DU) used in aeronautics may be found at the following website: www.abwem-wpafb.af.mil/em/emb/aircraft/default.htm.

POSTSCRIPTS 2003:
Concerning the Schipol accident mentioned above, a document by Van den Berg, dated 28 Feb. 2002, analyses the limits of the official inquiry (obtained from laka@antenna.nl).

New reports about civilian uses and potential uses of DU may be found at http://web.ead.anl.gov/uranium

Chapter 5

The Behaviour of Depleted Uranium in the Human Body

In Chapter 1, The Physics of Depleted Uranium and the Chemistry of Uranium, we stated that the chemical characteristics of all the isotopes of uranium are the same. This means that the problems associated with its behaviour in the human body are the same, whether for natural uranium (as it is found in uranium ore like pitchblende) or for depleted uranium. Under particular conditions of temperature, pressure, humidity and acidity, any isotope of uranium will form the same type of compounds. These compounds have the same degree of water solubility and, consequently, follow the same patterns of diffusion, transformation (metabolism), and excretion in the human body.

Extraction mines are the major site of exposure to natural uranium, containing uranium and all the products derived from the process of radioactive decay of its isotopes. Contamination can occur through the skin or by the inhalation of very fine particles of ore (whose uranium content is usually very low: 2 to 4 g per tonne). Despite their better-controlled, less dangerous conditions, contamination can also occur in uranium enrichment plants, and where metallic uranium is used in the making of industrial products.

Exposure to DU is greatest on battlefields and in regions devastated by war (see chapter 3, Military Uses of DU, and chapter 4, Non-military Uses of DU). Entire populations can be endangered, because the regions affected can be much greater than those where military missiles and DU-armed vehicles were actually used.

The DU that enters the human body from these different sources then undergoes various metabolic processes according to its physico-chemical form (soluble or insoluble). Entering the body by inhalation, ingestion, through the skin, or present in the form of surgically inextricable shrapnel, it can concentrate in different organs and pose various health problems, as we shall see in chapter 6:

The Effects of DU on Health

1. Contamination from deteriorating war materials
After conflict, there is a serious contamination risk to the resident population from deteriorating fragments of missiles and plating from armoured vehicles remaining on and in the ground.

The UNEP report (UNEP 2001) analyses a small number of DU penetrators (seven complete penetrators and one fragment) found in Kosovo in regions heavily bombed by NATO, on the ground surface or at different depths beneath it. These are non-exploded missiles, some of which were deeply embedded in the ground. When UNEP's scientific team visited the site of operations in November 2000, these missiles had been abandoned, or remained embedded, and had therefore been in contact with the earth and the surface waters of the area for nearly eighteen months.

During this period, these missiles had undergone chemical degradation: 'A large percentage of the DU missiles which have hit soft targets or have missed their targets altogether penetrate the ground, where outside agents will corrode them (to a variable extent, depending on the local environmental circumstances).' 'This may result in the contamination of the groundwater and drinking water.' 'Penetrators currently hidden in the ground may be dug up during construction work in the future'.

The contamination is essentially due to the fact that '... the missile-heads oxidise and their surface layer can easily detach and contaminate the ground. DU has been found at depths of up to 30cm, coming from a missile-head on the surface'.

It therefore seems that the major risk of chemical contamination from metallic DU left on battlefields is in its subsequent degradation, on exposure to air and soil, into oxides (soluble and insoluble) and other chemical compounds.

While the military use of DU was still being investigated, the United States military had studied this point in detail (see, for example, Elder et al., 1980).

2. Contamination from shrapnel lodged in the body

Contamination can occur because fragments of DU (shrapnel) have penetrated the body through a wound, and their position makes surgical removal impossible. Experiments implanting DU fragments in rats have identified kidneys and bones as preferential sites for DU deposits in the body. Increased concentrations were also found in the brain, testes and lymph nodes.

Since there was a certain number of accidents during the Gulf War caused by US missiles (US armoured vehicles destroyed by US DU missiles, US armoured vehicles with DU plating destroyed by 'friendly fire'), the US Department of Defense has been able to study and follow DU-contaminated veterans for several years (DoD, 2000,

Table P; see also Hooper et al., 1999). 'Fifteen veterans had multiple tiny [metallic DU] fragments scattered in their muscles and soft tissues.'

These fragments could not be surgically removed without causing extensive damage to the surrounding tissues ... In the 15 veterans with retained fragments, the mean uranium level was about 150 times higher than the mean uranium level of the 18 veterans with no fragments'. It has also been observed that these very strong concentrations last for at least a year, from which it is concluded that the excretion of uranium from metallic fragments is slow and subject to metabolic control.

3. Contamination from aerosols

In the impact of a DU missile (a penetrator) on a hard target, or of a missile against the DU plating of an armoured vehicle, particles of DU are released in aerosol form (ceramic compounds, essentially oxides).

It is known that a large part of the DU contained in a penetrator becomes an aerosol made up of tiny particles of uranium oxide (see, in particular, DoD 2000, Table M). The amount of DU released in this form varies from 40% to 70%, according to the form of the missile, the metal of its casing (tungsten or other) and the hardness of the target. This dust then falls on the battlefield, covering the ground and the wrecks of the armoured vehicles. It is lifted and transported long distances by the wind and can penetrate deep into the ground, carried by surface water and rain.

Inhaling this dust is probably one of the principal sources of contamination. Studies of uranium miners after autopsy have shown a significantly high quantity of uranium in the lung tissue (WHO 2001, chapter 7).

Observation of US Gulf War veterans shows that '... in accordance with previous studies, a high percentage of breathable dust from the impact [of DU missiles] on hard targets is found in the form of soluble oxides in the lungs' (DoD 2000, Table M). Apart from the few cases of veterans carrying DU fragments integrated into their tissue, inhalation seems to be the major means of contamination in US and British veterans of the Gulf War. This is why programmes have been set up to study them: by monitoring the excretion of uranium in their urine, one can research the possible accumulation of uranium in the body (DoD, 2000; Durakovic et al., 2001; MoD, 2000; Roth et al., 2001, Sharma, 2001, UMRC, 2001). However, some doubt remains as to the interpretation of urinary uranium levels as indications of contamination: '...it is difficult to infer body load of uranium from blood and urine levels' (Medact, 2001).

It should be noted that no comparable study concerning the Iraqi veterans or the civilian population of Iraq seems to have been set up by the US or British governments (responsible for the contamination), or by the United Nations. In addition, a country like Iraq – which is impoverished, and subject to embargo – cannot conduct 24-hour isotopic or radiological analysis of urine (as is necessary to distinguish natural uranium – always present in urine – from DU).

Contamination can also occur through the ingestion of contaminated dust, either through direct contact during reconstruction or agricultural work, or through children putting dirty fingers to their mouths. In this mode of contamination, the ingestion of the dust seems to be followed by rapid elimination in stools. The small amount of soluble DU re-absorbed by the intestinal epithelium reaches the kidney through the bloodstream. It is then rapidly and efficiently excreted in urine (about 90% in a few days).

The ingestion of contaminated dust seems therefore to be the mode of contamination that leads to the least accumulation in the organs. 'Soluble uranium (natural or depleted) which is absorbed in the blood circulation within the body is eliminated rapidly through the kidneys in urine. About 67% is excreted within the first day without being deposited in any organ. Approximately 11% is initially deposited in the kidneys and excreted with a 15 day half-life. Most of the remaining 22% is initially deposited in the bone (up to 20%), which is the principal storage site in the body, and the rest is distributed to other organs and tissues. Uranium deposited in the bones and other organs is subsequently released back into the bloodstream with at least two different half-lives, both longer than the excretion half-life for the kidney. Similar to other heavy metals (such as mercury) causing neurotoxic problems, uranium can cross the blood-brain barrier ... studies with laboratory animals ... found uranium in the placenta, foetus, and milk' (Zajic, 2001, Ch. 8; see also Priest, 2001; for a critique of Priest's article, see Bramhall, 2001).

Finally, dust can contaminate through the skin. Laboratory research on animals has shown that soluble uranium compounds (particularly nitrates) can penetrate the body through the skin. In certain studies, contamination through the skin resulted in the death of the animals (rabbits), due to renal failure. The oxides created at the moment of impact are largely non water-soluble, but the transformations which they then undergo in the atmosphere and in

64

the ground can easily result in soluble compounds (chlorides, nitrates etc.) which can therefore penetrate the body in this way.

4. Water contaminated by oxide derivatives

Oxides formed at the moment of impact are largely non water-soluble, which does not prevent them from being transported by water. In conditions of adequate acidity and temperature, they can become soluble (see Fig. 3.2 in WHO 2001; see also UNEP, 2001, Appendix V: Possible Effects of DU on Groundwater). Thus they can be transported deep in the ground, in streams, ponds and wells, even at considerable distance from the battlefield. Their presence in surface water may make them more likely to enter the food chain. The UNEP report on Kosovo, for example, found that DU was beginning to be incorporated into lichens and the bark of trees (UNEP 2001, Appendix VI: Lichen as a bio-indicator of DU).

This phenomenon, and the potential presence of soluble DU compounds in drinking water, constitute a risk that civilian populations will be contaminated by ingesting DU. This would give rise to the situation described in point 3, which is considered probably the least dangerous of the possible modes of contamination.

Theoretically, a toxic substance can become concentrated when passing up the food chain, increasing the risk to the next consumer in the chain. In his book, Christophe de Brouwer writes 'The possibility of uranium or plutonium becoming concentrated through the trophic chain would obviously be catastrophic, since a few traces of the element could give rise to the possibility of very considerable concentrations reaching man. Fortunately, this is not the case. Actinides [and therefore uranium] are very poorly absorbed by the digestive tract. On the contrary, at each stage of the trophic chain, ingested actinides tend to be mainly re-dispersed into the environment. Only a small fraction reaches animals or man, thus preventing the phenomenon of large-scale concentrations'. But the author goes on: 'There may be exceptions and surprises. For instance, the compound into which the isotope is inserted may be particularly liposoluble ... or certain species, notably plant species, may, in spite of everything, concentrate uranium, as seems to be the case in spruces or lichen' (De Brouwer, 2001; see also Castanier et al., 2001).

A final word on a problem commonly discussed: the possibility of decontaminating veterans (and, it is to be hoped, civilian populations also) contaminated by DU. A very detailed bibliographical study on this topic may be found in Durakovic, 1999; the results are still uncertain, but some methods seem promising: 'The possibility of treating an internal uranium contamination with complexing agents is linked to the ability of a ligand to form non-iodised cyclic complexes with inorganic ions, complexes which are then eliminated through the kidneys. This treatment must begin as soon as possible [after contamination] before the uranium is incorporated in the target organs. Indeed, once actinides [of which uranium is one] enter a cell, the hydrophilic ligands cannot cross the cell wall (which is hydrophobic) to reach them. Research at present centres on the possibility of synthesising lipophilic chelating agents, which could reach the unwanted radioactive elements inside the cells, and thus encourage their excretion through the kidneys.'

To write this chapter we have consulted, in particular, DHC 2001; Durakovic 1999, 2001; Harley et al., 1999, ch. 2; NRPB 2001, Q6: When is DU harmful?, Q7: What happens to DU inside the body?; UNEP 2001; VISIE 2001; WHO 2001, ch. 6: Case studies and exposure scenarios, ch. 7: Behaviour of uranium in the body, ch. 10: Biokinetics of uranium after internal exposure, WISE 2001; Zajic 1999.

Chapter 6

The Effects of Depleted Uranium
on Human Health

In chapter 5, while discussing the metabolisation of DU, we mentioned the different ways by which it can contaminate the human body and briefly surveyed current knowledge about the paths by which it can enter the body and remain there for longer or shorter periods, depending on the organ affected, before being eventually eliminated by urination.

The metabolisation of uranium occurs no matter which isotope has entered the body, but the risks for the person contaminated depend on the particular isotope in question as well as on its chemical form and the particular organ where it lodges, at least temporarily. These differences result from the different sensitivities of the organs affected by toxic substances, and also from uranium's 'double toxicity': one toxicity caused by its chemical nature (the same for every isotope) and another caused by the different physical characteristics (the radioactivity) of each isotope (see chapter one: The Physics of DU and the Chemistry of Uranium). For these reasons we must distinguish between the risks of chemical poisoning produced by DU from those caused by its toxic radiation.

However, it is conceivable that the negative effects on health might interact or even reinforce one another. It has not been firmly established that they do not. Quite the contrary, one of the most important points in the current debate concerns the nonchalance with which most published analyses limit their consideration – usually so as to minimise the dangers – to one or other of these two factors, and fail to discuss their possible interaction. And it is not just a question of the possible interaction (synergy) between these two toxic features of DU, but also of the possible synergies between the effects of DU and those of all the other chemical and/or pathogenic agents to which humans are exposed in wartime. The website of Medact ('health professionals challenging barriers to health') states that:

> All these toxic agents could interact. It is well known that when two active drugs are given in routine medical practice, unexpected harmful interactions can occur.
>
> Interactions can be additive or even multiplicative. No one knows at present whether DU can interact with vaccines, insecticides or CW [chemical warfare] agents, and it would be impossible to find out except by planned observations in war situations. (Medact, 2001).

The lack of interest shown in possible synergies between the two toxicities of DU and those between DU and other toxic agents is the basis for the criticisms (Hooper, 2001) published by the CADU (Campaign Against Depleted Uranium, UK) in response to the Royal Society's recent report on the health hazards of DU munitions (RS, 2001), a report which will be discussed below.

1. Chemical toxicity
In general terms, the toxicity of uranium for any animal is that common to all heavy metals. In an article which tends to minimise the risks of DU, O.G. Raabe, Professor of Toxicology and Environmental Health at the University of California, writes:

> 'Lead is the most analogous metal to uranium. However, metallic lead is considerably more toxic than metallic uranium. Lead-based compounds are far more dangerous than uranium-based ones, which are not easily absorbed by the body. Lead affects the nervous system and several biochemical processes, whereas the uranyl ion does not interfere with important biochemical processes, except for its tendency to lodge in the renal tubes, where damage can result if the build-up [of uranium] is excessive' (Raabe, 2001).

Indeed it seems easy to minimise the dangers resulting from DU's toxicity, through the fact that the uranium oxides that are created by the impacts of a DU missile and a target – or of a missile and DU armour-plating – form a fine dust (an aerosol) of oxides that are not water-soluble. This dust seems to have few chances of entering the human organism (Marusic et al., 2001; Priest, 2001; for a critique of Priest's article, see Bramhall, 2001). Besides, it seems that we can eliminate quickly (in a matter or days) that fraction of the dust that has entered our bodies and been rendered soluble by metabolic action (See ch. 5 on metabolisation of uranium). But this is not risk-free: there is a risk of kidney damage or blocking of renal function. The DU particles that remain in the lungs could perhaps also contribute to the formation of cancers, by chemical means (independent from their radioactivity) – but here again the data and interpretations are contradictory.

There are other sources in the literature, however, which give a different scenario about uranium toxicity. For example, in the DU report of the US Department of Defense, ch. 3-A, Chemical Toxicity of Depleted Uranium, we read: 'The three uranium oxides of primary concern [those formed at impact] are relatively insoluble [in water], tending to dissolve slowly [weeks or years, according to the particular oxide] in bodily fluids. Once dissolved, uranium may react with biological molecules and, in the form of the uranyl ion, exert its toxic effects. According to research, the kidney is the organ most sensitive to chemical effects from excess uranium. Depending on the concentration of uranium in the kidney, these toxic effects may include damage and death of kidney cells, decreasing the kidney's ability to filter impurities from the blood.' (DoD, 2000).

The study published by the World Health Organisation is even less optimistic (WHO 2001, ch.8, The chemical toxicity of uranium, and Annex 5: Chemical toxicity of uranium; Occupational exposure standards after inhalation and the impact of the ICRP biokinetic model). After a detailed analysis of experiments on animals (subjected to uranium contamination by inhalation, by ingestion, by fragments through the skin), the report sums up current knowledge about contamination of humans.

Whereas 'the increase of cancer risk [through inhalation] for miners in uranium mines (and also tin and iron mines) has been attributed essentially to exposure to a product of uranium breakdown, radon', 'it has not yet been clarified which other toxic agents present in mines (including breathable particles of uranium dust) could be significant in the etiology of this illness'. As for ingestion, 'there are few data giving adequate descriptions of the dose-response ratio (the toxicity) of uranium ingested by humans.' But, for this type of contamination, the report seeks to be reassuring. As for fragments of metallic DU lodged in the body, 'the renal functions of Gulf War veterans with non-extractable DU fragments have remained normal, several years after their wounds, despite uranium concentrations in urine reaching 30.7 milligrams per gram of creatine [i.e. more than 100 times higher than normal]' (measures of filtration of plasmatic creatine show the efficiency of renal filtration). More worrying evidence comes from *in vitro* studies which have shown that 'cultures of human osteoblasts (cells that make bone) can be transformed, that is, modified into precancerous cells, in the presence of uranium. According to the authors, this transformation was due much more to the chemical effects [of uranium] than to the radioactivity.'

(More complete information on DU's chemical toxicity may be found in Durakovic, 1999; Priest, 2001; WISE, 2001, Uranium toxicity; and Zajic, 1999, ch.8: Chemical toxicity)

2. Radioactive toxicity

All the isotopes of uranium are radioactive and therefore unstable. The same is true of all the elements that make up their decay chains, until they become lead, which is stable. The specific debate over the risks of DU radioactivity is due to the fact that all these isotopes have very different half-lives, and emit particles of very diverse natures and energy levels. In future studies, it will also be necessary to bear in mind the possible traces of transuranic elements in the DU which has, until now, been used in the manufacture of arms and armour plating. On this point, see ch. 2: 'U-236, Plutonium and other transuranic elements in DU'.

An exhaustive presentation on the radioactive characteristics of DU and its effects can be found in Roussel, 2001. In particular, this text helps explain a point which is often ignored: the distinction between DU's activity as a radioactive source – its intensity, measured for example by the number of disintegrations per second – and its radioactive toxicity. The latter depends not only on intensity, but also on the nature of the particle emitted and its energy, on the target organ affected and its sensitivity, and even on the age of the person contaminated. Radioactive toxicity is measured in units of Sievert or 'rem', meaning radiation-equivalent-man (1 Sv = 100 rem). Useful information about this was provided to us by Sharma (Sharma, 2001).

It seems easy to downplay the dangers of DU (essentially, of U-238). Military spokespeople, diplomats and scientific institutions like the WHO are spreading the idea that the radioactivity of DU – at the point of manufacture – is 40% less than that of natural uranium (Priest 2001), which is quite correct. But it is still far from clear that this parameter (that is, the surrounding radioactivity caused by the presence of DU dust) is the only significant one with regard to its harmful effects.

Increasingly, models of the behaviour of microscopic DU particles in the body try to demonstrate that the essential parameter is rather the local effect of this weak radioactivity, within a radius of a few dozen cells; and that a particle trapped in tissue can cause severe local (especially chromosomal) damage. (A note at the end of this chapter: 'Busby's "second-event model"' briefly describes one of these theoretical hypotheses.)

At the cellular level, the emission of low-energy, low-intensity alpha particles during the decay of a uranium atom (U-238) and later disintegrations, can cause frequent mutations of cellular DNA (leading to genome instability). These serial impacts can reach not only the directly irradiated cells, but also the surrounding ones (the 'bystander effect'; see for example Iyer et al., 2000; Lenhert, 2001; Nagawawa et al., 1999).

If, for more on the dangers of DU radiation, we return to the US Department of Defense report previously mentioned (DoD 2000, ch. 3-B: Health effects of DU radiological toxicity), we find that there is apparently nothing to worry about. 'The low level of radiation emitted by DU and the results of scientific experiments show that DU does not cause bone cancer. Indeed, scientists have never observed bone cancer in populations exposed to any form of uranium, not even enriched uranium which is much more radioactive than DU'.

As for other health risks, the ATSDR [Agency for Toxic Substances and Disease Registry, USA] concludes that 'one need not fear health problems from inhaling or ingesting uranium, whether natural or depleted, because its radioactivity is very weak'. But in this matter, as with chemical toxicity, the WHO report is less optimistic (WHO 2001). It reveals that 'epidemiological studies show, repeatedly and convincingly, there are more numerous cases of lung cancer in uranium miners, but not of leukaemia. The IARC (International Agency for Research on Cancer), in its latest analysis of the effects of ionising radiation, classed the nuclides which produce particles (and which are deposited inside the human body) as carcinogens'. This is obviously the case for the aerosols of DU oxides previously discussed. Again, 'death from lung cancer among the workers of uranium enrichment plants is very high compared with national levels'. These results do not seem to match the statistical analysis presented by the Royal Society of London, whose team of experts undertook the dubious task of calculating the statistical averages from the epidemiological data on different cancer types in uranium miners (RS 2001, 2002). We shall return to the Royal Society report in the next chapter: 'Epidemiology of the effects of DU on the human body'.

To bring together the points made so far about the risks of the 'double toxicity of DU', we believe that current knowledge about the dangers of using DU and dispersing it in the environment is sufficient to dictate a policy of caution, both in military and non-military use. Furthermore, possible interaction between the two effects could make the situation even worse for the populations concerned: the weakening of immunity caused by toxic action could, in turn, increase the risk of pre-cancerous modifications developing under localised radioactivity.

People might also believe that the military, preoccupied with the need to develop arms with maximum efficiency, was unaware of these dangers. This was not the case.

In fact, the military knew about probable risks to human health from the 'double toxicity' of DU, which had been studied for a long time. Just after the Gulf War in May 1991, in response to questions from deputy Les Aspin, the US DoD admitted that DU use 'leaves residue that is oxidised by the atmosphere and/or corroded by water. The two processes can cause environmental pollution which, in theory, could have negative consequences for human health, firstly through groundwater' (cited in Arkin, 1993). This did not stop the US from using about 940,000 40mm DU-tipped missiles (launched by planes) and 4,000 105mm missiles (used by armoured cars) during the Gulf War, leaving a total of at least 400 tonnes of DU on Iraqi soil. Arkin comments, 'The Pentagon spent a considerable sum to recover armoured cars damaged by 'friendly fire' (that is, by US missiles) and to send their contaminated parts to South Carolina, as nuclear waste. But nothing was done in Iraq, and very little in Kuwait, to recover the remains of missiles. The problem remains unsolved'.

When US veterans of 'Operation Desert Storm' announced the first signs of 'Gulf War Syndrome', the DoD commissioned investigations into the problem. The most important report is the one published by the RAND Corporation (RAND, 1999). It is actually a combination of nine reports financed by the US military on 'the analysis of scientific literature on Gulf War Syndrome' (see the more detailed presentation of these reports in the Introduction).

The seventh volume discusses DU more specifically (Harley et al., 1999; for a critique, see 'RAND report and DU, bone accumulation and lung damage' in VISIE, 2001). From this quite comprehensive report, read in particular Chapter 2: 'Effects of internal or external DU exposure on human health' and Chapter 3: 'Toxic effects of uranium and radioactive effects of DU'. Among the conclusions, we find:

> Exposure to uranium and other heavy metals in large doses can cause changes in renal function and at very high doses result in renal failure. In spite of these findings, no increased morbidity or frequency of end-stage renal disease has been observed in relatively large occupational populations chronically exposed to natural uranium at concentrations above the normal ambient ones (RAND, 1999).

Further research is suggested: epidemiological studies of Gulf War veterans; research to define more accurately the risks to the populations concerned and understand better the workings of uranium on renal function; studies of secondary (beta and gamma) radiation caused by the products of the (alpha) decay of U-238.

International organisations, in theory created specifically to protect world health, have been surprisingly slow to grasp the seriousness of the situation that was created in 1991 when DU entered the arsenal of instruments of war. For example, it took almost a decade, after years of silence, and later, clumsy attempts to downplay the problem, for the World Health Organisation to decide to analyse the bibliographical data on this topic with any interest (WHO 2001).

We have already cited certain chapters of the WHO report on the chemical and radioactive aspects, which sometimes contradict the optimism of military-financed research. But no specific study has been undertaken on this subject; reference is always made to data focusing on uranium miners or nuclear establishments (gas diffusion factories, nuclear power stations, nuclear fuel reprocessing plants), or coming from military organisations. However, some doubt seems to remain, despite official optimism.

In the conclusion of the WHO report we read, 'the greatest potential for DU exposure will follow conflict where DU munitions are used and people living or working in these areas inhale dusts [produced by the impact of missiles], and consume contaminated food and drinking water. Measurements of DU in conflict areas indicate only localised (within a few tens of metres from impact sites) contamination at the ground surface. However, levels of contamination in food and drinking water could rise after some years and should be monitored where it is considered that there is a reasonable possibility of significant quantities of DU entering the groundwater or food chain.'

Even the Spiez Laboratory report, financed by the Swiss military, which begins with ironic comments about apocalyptic assertions by DU opponents, finishes with this sentence: 'This type of ammunition leaves long term pollution on battlefields that is incompatible with the standards of civilian protection from radiation' (Schmid et al. 2000).

The combination of the different data we have mentioned here allows us to specify the potential risks of DU exposure. These are the chemical toxicity of uranium, particularly the doubts over the time taken to eliminate it from the body, and the effects of DU radioactivity, particularly when it is intimately connected with tissue. If, moreover, we take into account the possible interaction of these two effects, we can see that military use, and probably also non-military use of DU, exposes the human body to still largely unpredictable dangers, and obliges entire populations to live in potentially unhealthy areas, long after conflict, for an extremely long time. Whatever one's interpretation of the 'precautionary principle', which is so talked about today, it is very clearly unacceptable to pursue such use of DU, or to intensify it. To use one of the last phrases of the RAND Report (Harley et al., 1999), 'the use of DU munitions and armor is likely to expand greatly over the coming years, both in the US military and in other countries.'

Therefore, the conclusions of Roussel may be considered eminently reasonable. 'With very reasonable and certainly not maximalist hypotheses, we have shown that the use of DU-charged shells can result in lasting danger to the environment and to neighbouring civilian populations. These dangers result firstly from the fragmenting of the shell into contaminating dust. The danger of the un-fragmented part of the charge remaining in bulk is smaller, but only if this part is quickly collected by appropriate organisations. Measurements, enquiries and studies from multidisciplinary teams are necessary'. (Roussel, 2001).

At this point in our understanding, one might have doubts on the subject of the effects of DU use, sometimes denounced as catastrophic and global, that are due to its chemical and radioactive toxicity. However, prudence is necessary because of uncertainties on both the scientific level (current situation of physiological studies on animals and humans) and the concrete level (including information on the section of DU that becomes aerosol at the point of impact, and on the factors of dispersion and solubilisation of uranium oxides in the environment).

Therefore, we must keep to the conclusion of De Brouwer: 'We cannot affirm that the irradiation increase caused by DU use will necessarily have short-term or mid-term consequences. Nevertheless, significant uncertainty remains regarding the long-term consequences for those people who are young and who will suffer this increased irradiation their whole lives. We know that there are some people who are more sensitive to ionising radiation: children, including unborn children, old people, and those who are genetically more susceptible; and other less-known circumstances can probably increase the risk.' De Brouwer, 2001). This seems relevant not only to the potential dangers of radioactivity, but also to those of the chemical toxicity of uranium.

Note on Dr. C. Busby's 'second-event model'.
Busby (Busby, 1995, 1998, 2000) suggested several years ago, and still defends, a model that describes the workings of radioactive particles

caught in tissue or cells. The model, initially developed for strontium (Sr-90) – an isotope produced during a nuclear explosion and therefore present in the radioactive fallout from atmospheric nuclear testing – can be generalised to all radioactive elements that are the source of a chain of radioactive decay (as is the case for uranium-238; see ch.1: The Physics of Depleted Uranium and the Chemistry of Uranium). Such a situation can be described as a series of bombardments by ionising particles of the cells or tissue where the radioactive particle is lodged, for instance, a particle of aerosol DU lodged in the alveoli of a lung.

In very simplified terms, we can summarise Busby's thesis as follows: the first radioactive event, a first alpha particle, might strike the nucleus of a cell and create a localised traumatism in its DNA (the chemical carrier of the body's genetic inheritance). The cell has mechanisms to repair its DNA. The activation of these mechanisms and the repair itself takes several hours. If a second disintegration takes place during this time, and the second particle passes through the same cellular nucleus (the probability of this depends on the cellular density of the tissue and the energy of the ionising particle), the traumatism can no longer be repaired and the cell will either die or sustain a mutation in its genetic inheritance. This could turn it into a pre-cancerous cell.

Busby's model has been quite strongly critiqued (Godhead, 1996; Edwards et al., 2000). However, what is disputed is not so much his general theoretical side, which is, on the contrary, considered plausible, but the fact that his calculations are wrong in several cases, the values being almost 10,000 times too great. Bearing in mind these corrections, it would seem that the risks of dangerous mutation provoked by such a 'second event' are small compared with the ongoing action on the body of radiation from natural radioactive elements always present in the body, and by the background gamma radiation. Even if these critiques are correct (and they have been partially accepted by Busby), the model seems to retain a certain validity, and could be the foundation for laboratory experiments that may help us understand some of the findings of the 'genome instability' previously mentioned.

POSTSCRIPT 2003: D. Garland's claims about adverse health effects on aerospace workers in the UK and USA may be found at www.du.publica.cz/papers/garland.htm

75

Chapter 7

The Epidemiology of the Effects of Depleted Uranium on the Human Body

Epidemiological information on the health of populations which have been exposed to uranium relates to various scenarios. In the two preceding chapters, we have seen that the degree to which uranium impacts on health depends on the conditions in which the contamination took place, and the uranium isotope involved.

Analysis of the relevant data pertaining to the survivors of the first nuclear explosion over Hiroshima (a U-235 fission bomb) is difficult due to the fact that several toxic and radioactive fission elements were present in the radioactive cloud that followed the explosion. All these elements had very different properties. Some useful information is available in Mould (2001).

The most detailed statistics covering a relatively long period (at least 20 years) describe the effects of working in uranium mines on the health of miners (the effects of toxicity and radioactivity in the mines) taking into account the length and conditions of work and the type of pathology observed. (See, for example, RS 2001, Table 6: 'Summary of mortality from various causes in uranium workers'; Durakovic 1999 contains a comprehensive bibliography on this topic, including an attempted synthesis).

On the topic of the effects of using uranium for military purposes, but used as a heavy metal (as opposed to a fissile element in nuclear bombs), the epidemiological data already gathered includes:
- factory workers involved in manufacturing metallic uranium, in particular DU. In the United States they have been monitored by the Energy Department (DoE, Fulco et al. 2000).
- US and British Gulf War veterans. In the United States they have been monitored by the US Department of Defense (DoD 2000) under the fairly close supervision of the American Gulf War Veterans' Association (AGWVA-BB 2001). In Great Britain, veterans have been followed up by the Ministry of Defence (MoD 2000).
- NATO troops in Kosovo. NATO and the US Department of Defense have set up a programme for monitoring veterans and training soldiers stationed in Kosovo (DoD 2001).

The state of health of the Iraqi populations which live near battlefields strewn with the debris of wrecked tanks and DU projectiles, especially those who live 'downwind' in areas where the prevailing winds carry the toxic clouds, is largely unknown. No proper epidemiological investigation has yet been carried out (see ch.9: Iraq). There is the same lack of information about the health of the Bosnians and Serbs.

Epidemiological studies are almost always instigated by a series of complaints made by individuals or small groups. These complaints tend to be thought of as subjective and therefore dubious – especially by the authorities. For example, when French ex-corporal Hervé Desplat 'lodged a complaint against the army for the illness he had suffered since [the Gulf War]', publishing his strong accusations in the French Communist Party's newspaper *L'Humanité* (Abdelkrim-Delanne 2000), people were reluctant to believe that DU lay at the root of his problems. But individual cases can multiply (see the many cases cited in Collon 2001) and can emerge as a problem shared by an identifiable group (for example, veterans of a particular battlefield or workers from a particular production line).

On top of these individual cases, several instances have provided warning that the possible presence of DU makes larger groups of people feel vulnerable, even if they are unable to prove that their problems are directly linked to the presence of DU. For example, the German village of Remscheid recorded 32 cases of cancer (including 17 fatal) after a US aeroplane, a Warthog A-10, most likely carrying DU weapons or ballast, crashed on the village on 7 December 1988 leaving 7 dead and 50 wounded (*Spiegel* 2001). In a case like this, it is hard for the inhabitants not to feel threatened by the toxic molecules and radioactive atoms that could still remain in the atmosphere. But how can a causal link between the plane crash and the cancers be established?

When individual complaints mount up and identifiable groups testify to experiencing the same malaise, it starts to be labelled a 'syndrome': for example, 'Gulf War Syndrome' or 'Balkans Syndrome'. Authorities then set up epidemiological studies of large populations.

It is interesting to examine the positions taken in recent epidemiological reports on DU, noting that these reports were published many years after the Gulf War. Protests from US and British Gulf War veterans, and veterans from the other NATO countries involved in Bosnia and Serbia have, at least partially, raised public interest in the issue. However, the big UN organisations have remained unmoved by the suffering of the Iraqi population.

There are weaknesses and methodological deficiencies in these reports. These are probably due, in part, to the difficulties inherent in the task, given the blurry definition of a 'syndrome'. In this hazy concept, objectively measured conditions (the level of DU in urine, potential kidney lesions, the incidence of certain cancers compared to the incidence expected in a similar, non-contaminated sample) are mixed with more subjective symptoms (eg. tiredness, muscle pains, difficulty concentrating, insomnia, stress). Even when there is reasonably 'objective' scientific data, such as the death rate for a certain type of cancer, these methodological deficiencies could equally be used to minimise the problem, to submerge it in such a wide context that the key phenomena sought are not found.

1. Uranium workers

An example of the dubious use of statistical methodology is found in the recent report by the Royal Society of London (RS 2001, 2002). In Annex I: 'Mortality from various causes in uranium workers', the incidence of death due, for example, to different types of cancer is compared to the rates of death from these same cancers in the general population ($I = O/A$, where $O =$ deaths of uranium workers and $A =$ average number of deaths in the general population of the same age group). The weighted averages were calculated using the results of epidemiological studies from 1983 to 2000. Each of these studies involved between 10 and 1849 cases.

The results seem to be clear, but do they have any meaning? If the results are valid, the conclusion could be drawn that working with uranium is good for one's health! Within the statistical margin of error, for all deaths, $I = 0.86$ (between 0.79 and 0.93). Even considering the deaths from different cancers, $I = 0.91$ (between 0.85 and 0.97). More specifically, for lung cancer, which can very plausibly be associated with inhaling toxic and radioactive particles, $I = 0.94$ (between 0.83 and 1.05). In almost every case, $I < 1$, which confirms that uranium workers are, on average, in better health than the general population.

The exercise is dubious. For example, research and diagnosis methods changed between 1983 and 2000, and the average age of the populations also changed. To have used the weighted averages method in this case seems rather absurd. These results contradict numerous other epidemiological studies which all find, at least for lung cancer, a greater number of deaths among uranium workers (miners and manufacturing workers) than in the general population (see Mould 2001, Priest 2001).

2. The Gulf War

Since the Gulf War (1991), the only identifiable group that has been regularly monitored is the veterans, especially the US veterans. In this case, there are two large populations to compare: the veterans who were in the Gulf and had entered Kuwait and Iraq during or after the military operations (about 500,000 people); and those veterans who stayed in or near Saudi Arabia (about 200,000) who, in theory, have no reason to be contaminated by DU. At the end of February 2000, of the 133,000 veterans on the US Defense Department's medical register, about 80% were suffering from symptoms corresponding to the widest definition of 'Gulf War Syndrome' (VA 2000).

These large-scale epidemiological studies were not limited to or specifically designed for researching possible negative effects of DU. The general and rather vague task was to research the possible etiological causes of the 'Gulf War Syndrome'. This led to twelve simultaneous research studies (literature reviews not epidemiological studies) commissioned by US military personnel from the RAND Corporation (RAND 1999; see the Introduction to these 'open-ended chapters' for a list of the themes investigated in RAND reports). Only one of RAND's twelve reports focused on the possible effects of DU (Harley et al. 1999). One other literature review on previously gathered epidemiological data was then undertaken by the Institute of Medicine (IOM, USA) (Fulco et al. 2000) with funding from the Department of Defense.

An initial report on the US veterans (EPI 1994) seems to have been prompted by data from Great Britain:

'A recent report by the United Kingdom Atomic Energy Authority warned about possible long-term consequences of depleted uranium (DU) left on the battlefield in the Persian Gulf. As a result, [US] Congress directed the Army Environmental Policy Institute to conduct a study to determine:
1. The health and environmental consequences of using DU on the battlefield;
2. Which remediation technologies exist or might be developed to clean up DU contamination;
3. Ways to decrease DU toxicity;
4. How to best protect the environment from the long-term consequences of DU use.'

This report publishes its 'results in brief', one of which is rather surprising, given the exploratory nature of the exercise: 'It is highly unlikely that DU is a contributing factor to the unexplained illnesses currently being reported by veterans of Desert Storm.' But this report cannot be considered an epidemiological study as it simply discusses the possible consequences of DU on the health of soldiers, relying only on the scientific or empirical knowledge of the time. Its conclusions are based on '...the experimental data [what data?] and the lessons learned in Operation Desert Storm...'.

Following this, there were a series of studies on small populations or specific topics, for example: deformities in children; women soldiers or veterans' wives having miscarriages. (In ch. 9: Iraq, we will discuss some of these partial epidemiological studies in more detail.). A short summary is available in Mould 2001.

A wider group of studies, with the specific objective of researching the impact of DU on the physical health of British Gulf War veterans, was undertaken by the British Ministry of Defence (MoD 1999). However, this study was only concerned with putting in place suitable technology, and determining potentially useful tests for detecting the presence of uranium and distinguishing naturally occurring uranium from DU. The study also investigated more sophisticated tests on the state of kidney functioning.

In 2000, the Ministry published the report of the first real epidemiological study on British Veterans of the Gulf War (MoD 2000). The report describes a number of studies undertaken at several universities. One of them (University of Manchester), which investigated the deaths of veterans randomly chosen from a population of 9 600 and auxiliaries chosen from a population of 4,800, stated that:

'The number of deaths and the causes of death are the same for the veterans who were involved in the Gulf War as those who were not. The slightly higher number of deaths among the veterans seems to be mainly due to vehicle accidents. We have not found anything worrying, excessive or unusual in the deaths of the Gulf War veterans who have passed away since the end of the conflict.' (Macfarlane et al. 2000)

This study was published in *The Lancet*. However, another study (Guy's, King's and St Thomas' School of Medicine, financed jointly by the British Ministry of Defence and the US Defense Department) examined the 'subjective' side of the illnesses experienced by Gulf War veterans chosen at random from 4,250 veterans and 'control' soldiers. This study found that:

'The British Gulf War veterans were up to three times more likely than the control group to complain of various symptoms.' (Ismal et al.1999)

The causes of these frequent illnesses are still unknown. This study was also published in *The Lancet*.

In the United States, the first report expressing concerns about the health of veterans was made by the Committee for Veteran Affairs (USSCVA 1998) at the request of the Senate. It contains hard-hitting points about the lack of preparation, knowledge and information given out by the military authorities about the pathological situations they were creating on the battlefield. The report is very critical of the military hierarchy, but it does not give epidemiological results. More recently, a Defense Department report (HRAC 2000) gives extremely detailed technical points on the presumed doses, battle scenarios, and sources and routes of contamination, only to observe: 'there exists a gap between the empirical data and knowledge'.

Not until the December 2000 report (DoD 2000, ch. V: 'Follow-up') was more information available. This report started with a fairly clear statement:

'Since the Gulf War the effectiveness of DU weaponry has encouraged the proliferation of these weapons in allied and enemy arsenals. There is therefore no doubt that DU will be used on battlefields in future conflicts against US soldiers.'

So there is a need to be better informed on the post-conflict effects of these weapons.

Amongst the conclusions:

'The VA [Department of Veterans' Affairs] has not established that there are negative effects on kidney function and only slight malfunctioning of the reproductive and central nervous systems in veterans carrying fragments of DU in their bodies and with high levels of uranium in their urine.'

There were 68 victims of 'friendly fire' identified in 1998 by the military administration; the VA made contact with 48 of them. This study was however limited to the 33 who agreed to participate in the study starting in 1999, 15 of whom had uranium fragments in their bodies. Later the number of identified victims of 'friendly fire' had risen to 104, of whom 99 agreed to participate in control programmes.

As for the 100,000 other veterans who have complained of one or other of the symptoms of 'Gulf War Syndrome', there is still doubt:

'It is unlikely that exposure to DU is the cause of the undiagnosed illnesses affecting Gulf War veterans.' (PSOB 1999)

These conclusions have been severely criticised by Fahey (2000). The American Veterans' Association has also strongly protested:

'When thousands of Gulf War veterans started to notice thousands of health problems, the Pentagon quickly ruled out the link to DU (and chemical weapons, vaccinations against anthrax, etc.). From the beginning, the Pentagon underestimated the number of veterans who had been or who might have been contaminated with DU.' (AGWVA-BB 2001).

Meanwhile, the long-term consequences of the Gulf War within Iraq, and particularly the role of DU contamination on the current health situation there, have been hidden. The Iraqi authorities have been proclaiming for a decade (and to no avail) that DU contamination has caused illnesses, malaises and deformities. A genuine, independent study over a long period is obviously necessary. This study would involve examining all the pathological phenomena which seem to be becoming more and more acute in Iraq. The study would need to take into account other etiological factors due to the war and sanctions: malnutrition, lack of basic medicine, lack of water and hygiene, difficulties with vaccination campaigns, etc.

Some alarming documents reveal the increasing risks to which the Iraqi population is exposed, especially in the southern regions of the country ('downwind') which appear to have been the most affected by toxic and radioactive clouds coming from the battlefields. Among the earliest documents is a report of a meeting in Baghdad in 1998 (Lopez 1998). Since then there has been a fairly thorough epidemiological study exploring the relationship between DU contamination and the incidence of cancers in children younger than 15 during the period 1990-1999 in the Basra region of southern Iraq. The conclusions seem overwhelming:

'There has been a 100% increase in the incidence of different forms of leukaemia between 1990 and 1999; if all cancers are included, there has been a 242% increase between 1990 and 1999.' (Yacoup et al. 2000)

Several later visits by western specialists have confirmed the statistically significant increase in cancers and deformities in children in the southern regions of Iraq. One of the last visits was made by Ulrich Gottstein on behalf of the International Physicians for the Prevention of Nuclear War (Gottstein 2001). But until now there has been no serious commitment to a comprehensive, international and independent evaluation of the health situation in Iraq, nor for setting up a long term epidemiological study. Only in the last few months has

the WHO finally taken the necessary steps to get this project off the ground. On 13 April 2001, the WHO announced: 'Iraq and the WHO agree to investigate the effects of radiation'.
We are still waiting for action.

3. The NATO operations in Bosnia (1995) and Serbia (1999)
In late 2000 an announcement was made by the nations which had taken part, as NATO members, in the interventions in Bosnia and Serbia, which include Kosovo (see ch. 10 'Bosnia' and ch. 11 'Serbia'). It said that among their veterans there had been 24 deaths from leukaemia, and a large number of other illnesses – people spoke of the 'Balkans syndrome'. Almost all these countries then set up procedures for monitoring the health of every veteran presenting with aspects of the syndrome.

The US Department of Defense adopted a clear position: ' After the Italian media reported allegations of increased leukaemia among Italian soldiers in the Balkans, the international media promptly reported increases in other countries, and associated these with the DU used by NATO in Bosnia and Kosovo. Although later research rejected any link between leukaemia and DU with regard to the Balkans veterans and did not confirm any abnormal incidence of leukaemia, these accusations heightened the health concerns felt by veterans and their families, after their return from the Balkans.' (DoD-Ip 2001. This document is important because it gives references to most of the official military documents on the subject).

During a NATO press conference in Brussels a NATO spokesman, Mark Laity – encouraged by the optimistic assurances of a NATO physician, Dr Michael Kilpatrick – made fun of the opponents of the military use of DU: 'Now I know a lot of that stuff [presented in the press conference] is fairly undramatic, but it's what it's about, it's the calm, careful, scientific study. There's been a lot of fuss, a lot of copy, a lot of material written about DU, but the answer [to the journalists' questions] lies in the kind of studies being referred to here – careful, calm study.' (NATO-B 2001). The 'calm, careful' epidemiological studies to which Laity and Kilpatrick referred were those claiming to show that there was no connection between DU contamination and cancers (particularly leukaemia) among Gulf War veterans. They implied that therefore there could be none related to DU contamination in Bosnia and Kosovo.

A NATO communiqué confirmed this position: 'To date, the scientific and medical research continues to disprove any link between

Depleted Uranium and the reported negative health effects. Furthermore, the present evidence strongly suggests that NATO troops serving in the Balkans are not suffering negative health effects different from those suffered by their colleagues who have not served in the Balkans.' (NATO-BI 2001).

The Western governments which had protested energetically in January 2001, asking NATO to undertake epidemiological studies on the veterans and peacekeepers who had served in Bosnia and Kosovo, and more generally on the long term effects of the DU used by NATO, are now astonishingly silent. It seems that the leukaemia cases have vanished and so has the shouting.

We might have expected the governments of the countries bombarded – Bosnia and Kosovo – to express stronger and more polemical views. But there is total silence also from this quarter. Do they fear (financial) reprisals from the West?

What reports we do receive from Bosnia are also infrequent and unverifiable – but they are serious. We can cite the data sent by Dubravca Vujanovic, who speaks of the village of Bratunac (in the Serbian sector of Bosnia) which, after the Dayton Accords, became a refuge for Serbs from the outskirts of Sarajevo (the Hadzici district, hit by DU bombs in 1995 and 1996) : 'The village is empty, the cemetery is full ... the long-term inhabitants of Bratunac are alive, those who came from Hadzici are dying ... In 1998 there were many more deaths than births ... Almost 200 people in Bratunac have died of cancer...' (Vujanovic 2001). We must qualify these claims, however, by noting the remarks by Slavica Jovanovic, who was principal doctor of Bratunac's mobile consultation service. She states that 'a large number of corpses have been exhumed in Bosnia and transferred to Bratunac cemetery by the families'. According to the *Morgenpost* and the *Tagesspiel* of January 20 and 21, 2001, Slavica Jovanovic lost her job after she talked to journalists about the consequences of NATO strikes on the health of local populations.

We have also found, in a report sent by Zoran Zuza from Banja Luka (in the Serb sector of Bosnia), some epidemiological data provided by Dr Nemanja Veljkov concerning the Kasin Dol hospital and the cancers observed there: '1995 (43 patients, 22 deaths), 1999 (216 patients, 44 deaths), 2000 (240 patients, 73 deaths)' (Zuza 2001).

Only an independent epidemiological study – independent of NATO, Western governments and the Bosnian and Serb governments – will be able to shed more light on a scenario that is dramatic but unfortunately unverifiable.

Let us mention also a strange announcement from the International Atomic Energy Agency (IAEA), a recent statement saying that, in accordance with its statute, it holds 'a specific mandate to establish, in consultation and collaboration with the other UN agencies, international standards for protection against ionising radiation and the safety of radiation sources, and for monitoring the application of these standards. These standards cover a wide spectrum of situations... including the risks presented by DU' (IAEA 2001). It is not clear what motivated this unusual announcement, or what its purpose is. Up till now, in all discussions of DU, the IAEA had remained totally absent and passive, as if it was happy to leave this burning issue in the hands of the WHO. Does this announcement represent a late change of heart?

Chapter 8

The Effects of Depleted Uranium on the Environment

This chapter will not cover all the ways in which DU could potentially modify the environment, or all the predictable and direct effects on water, fauna, and flora etc. that occur when several tonnes of a radioactive heavy metal are present on limited surfaces and at depths which could, in time, become quite considerable. These are modifications and effects that could last thousands if not millions of years, and the risks they pose (although minimal at present) are hard to evaluate in the long term.

We will restrict ourselves here to the short-term modifications and effects, which are easier to predict, and which, judging by the scientific assessments currently possible, have negative consequences for human health. They include not only a serious decrease in the quality of drinking water in the contaminated regions, but also the presence of uranium, or some of its many chemical compounds, in the human food chain.

First of all, here is a text prepared by the WHO in January 2001 and distributed by NATO, which cannot be accused of bias against the military uses of DU; it is an extract from 'Background Material on Depleted Uranium' (Repacholi 2001):

> DU in the environment. In arid regions, the greater part of the DU remains on the surface in the form of dust. In regions with high rainfall, however, it readily penetrates the ground. Agricultural activity in contaminated regions can pose a risk to health, but that is likely to be a limited one. The chemical toxicity is expected to present more significant risks than the radioactivity. It is tentatively predicted that children would be more exposed than adults to contamination of water and food, once the regions contaminated by military action return to normality, because children's common activities during play, such as often putting their hands to their mouths, could lead to a greater ingestion of DU.

The potential of DU to cause environmental problems and consequent risks for human health is certainly not a new discovery, let alone an arbitrary claim made by opponents of its use; we can read, for example, the 'Summary Report to Congress on Health and Environmental Consequences of Depleted Uranium Use by the US Army' (EPI 1994), which declares:

If providing the fighting soldier with the maximum battlefield advantage means using DU, then methods to minimize potential health and environmental consequences must be employed. It should be noted that under current international law, there is no legal requirement to remediate environmental damage to battlefields. Furthermore, it is unlikely that future remediation of battlefields solely to remove DU will be required.

(In Chapter 13 'International Laws and Conventions and the Use of DU', we will give examples of the nonchalant way the great powers treat the rules of war and the relevant international treaties – often treaties that they have ratified.)

The report continues thus:

Uranium, like other metals, will oxidize under most environmental conditions. Variables such as temperature, metal fragment size and shape, presence or absence of coatings, and water and soil contaminants control the oxidation rate. Under some conditions, such as those in swamps and wetlands, DU oxidizes to a state where it will not readily dissolve in water and thus becomes relatively immobile. Under other conditions, such as on the surface of the ground or in shallow water, DU oxidizes to a state where it can dissolve and become mobile in water. Small DU particles, such as fragments and abrasion particles, will oxidize faster; large pieces, such as nearly whole penetrators and large fragments, will oxidize more slowly. Water is the dominant mechanism for transporting all metals, including DU, in the environment; metals may move in surface waters or groundwater. For metals widely dispersed across a land surface, the principal concern is groundwater contamination, although erosion can result in contaminated water runoff to surface streams and ponds. In arid environments, the wind can transport dust contaminated with small DU particles.

As you can see, the Environmental Policy Institute (EPI) of the US Army was already aware, probably well before 1994, of the dangers to the environment – and therefore to human health – of battlefields becoming polluted through the use of DU weapons; and we note that the word 'battlefields' is very restrictive, given the acknowledged possibility that this pollution could be spread by the wind over much greater areas and pass through the groundwater into distant streams, aquifers, and wells. In 1994 it had to admit that 'DU may become mobile in the environment'; but that did not prevent the USA from spreading 400 tonnes of DU over Iraq in 1991, or prevent NATO, in 1995 and 1999, from spreading 40 tonnes of DU over Bosnia and Yugoslavia.

Apart from the lessons drawn from the Gulf War and the studies

87

made in Kuwait and on the Iraqi battlefields, the EPI already had an extensive knowledge of the probable environmental contamination caused by DU. This is because it monitored the state of the soil, groundwater and atmosphere in and above several bases both in the USA and abroad (for the foreign bases, see Chapter 11 'Okinawa, Panama, Vieques and other US Bases').

In particular, experiments using DU 'penetrator' projectiles were conducted for several years on at least three sites in the USA: Aberdeen (Maryland), Jefferson (Indiana) and Yuma (Arizona).

The example of the Jefferson Proving Ground (subsequently decommissioned) is a good one:

> From 1984 to 1994, the licensee conducted accuracy testing of depleted uranium (DU) tank penetrator rounds at the site [the Jefferson Proving Ground]. The DU penetrator rounds vary in size but can be generally described as rods comprised of a DU titanium alloy with a diameter of approximately 2.5 cm and a length as much as 61 cm. The DU munitions testing contaminated approximately 5,100,000 square meters (1260 acres) on the site with an estimated 70,000 kg [70 tonnes!] of DU ... Currently, the licensed material is kept onsite in the restricted area known as 'Depleted Uranium Impact Area'. This area ... is located north of the firing line, and consists of approximately 12,000,000 square meters (3000 acres) (FR 1999).

As for the contamination of the Aberdeen base caused by DU (and four other chemical contaminants), this must have caused a lot of problems, because a very detailed study was ordered in 1998 to examine 'potential dangers resulting from a fire' (Williams et al., 1998); after a fire in the base they feared that contaminants had been dispersed.

Can one doubt that the US military was already aware, well before the Gulf War and the bombing of Bosnia and Yugoslavia, of the potential dangers of environmental contamination from the oxidation of DU and its pyrophoric properties?

Yet it took an avalanche of complaints from the US veterans of the Gulf War, reporting 'Gulf War Syndrome' (see Chapters 6 and 9, 'Health Effects of DU' and 'Iraq') and attributing it – at least in part – to DU contamination, before the US Department of Defense set up a commission of inquiry 'to study these cases and the circumstances surrounding potential causes'. This was the 'Gulf War Illnesses' commission, which included the 'environmental situation' among the questions to be examined. A first report appeared in 1998, a second fuller version in 2000 (EXP 2000). They contain not a word about the fate of Iraqi soldiers or civilians, but one does find a certain concern that 'since US forces used more than 300 tonnes of DU munitions in the Gulf War, it is reasonable to expect the entire battlefield was contaminated with dangerous levels of uranium aerosols, which could have exposed hundreds of thousands of Gulf War participants to harmful DU amounts.' The report describes a series of analyses made in Kuwait and Iraq between 1991 and 1998 on soil and atmospheric contamination 'in areas where US personnel lived'; it is a little surprising that the 'sampling did not include major tank battlefield areas where DU was fired or [Iraqi] targets struck.' Given this limitation, which is quite a significant one, the findings were negative: 'Any dose assessments calculated using the measured radionuclide concentrations from air filter samples are well below US regulatory limits for the general public.'

A more subtle report comes from the United Nations Environment Programme, which studied the situation in Kosovo after NATO had used DU penetrators during the 1999 war (UNEP 2000). More than 30,000 of these projectiles, containing almost 10 tonnes of DU, had been used in Kosovo, being dropped on over 120 sites in strikes against the underground fortifications on the Yugoslav-Albania border (see Annex VIII of the report – the list of coordinates given by NATO).

We note, however, that UNEP visited only eleven of the sites struck by DU munitions (a total of 12% of all sites where NATO admits having used them); and that only seven DU penetrators were found and analysed, plus a projectile fragment and six metal sheaths. No trace was found of tens of thousands of other projectiles used on these sites. If they missed their targets, they still lie buried in the ground (it is thought that nearly 90% of projectiles released from aircraft in combat miss their targets). And those that did hit their targets were transformed, at least partly, into aerosols.

Here are some of the report's conclusions: 'Even if the environmental risks at these sites are not alarming ... the appropriate authorities should undertake the marking of all DU-affected sites, where and when appropriate, until the site is cleared from solid DU (penetrators and jackets) ... Contamination points should be decontaminated where feasible and justified ... Within and adjacent to areas where DU has been used, groundwater used for drinking should be checked by the appropriate authorities for possible DU contamination.'

Two of the Annexes give better analysis of the dangers: the possible effects of DU on groundwater (Annex V) and the contamination of lichens, which can be used as bio-indicators of DU (Annex VI). They observe that 'some of the uranium is carried [by water into the ground] in the form of colloids. It is possible that the uranium concentration will increase in future, as the buried projectiles and their oxidation products continue to dissolve.' As for the food chain, they observe that samples of lichen and bark gathered in these areas show radioactivity levels which 'clearly indicate a contribution from DU. The presence of DU [in these samples] is due to the prior presence of DU in the air, which implies that at least some of the projectiles hit their targets, fragmented and produced air-borne dust.'

It is clear that lichens and some kinds of bark are early links in the food chain, and that a concentration of DU in them can lead to higher concentrations in food produced at these places (for the average levels of natural uranium in the environment, in the ground and in food, for comparison with those found by UNEP in Kosovo, see WHO 2001, Annex 3). Another fragile link in the food chain was identified in a scientific conference in Athens (Euler 2001): DU can pass from polluted water in rivers and ponds into organisms that live in the muddy riverbeds and which form the basis for the food intake of fish and freshwater molluscs.

As a whole, the UNEP report shows the very vague state of current knowledge (both empirical and theoretical) about the behaviour of uranium in the environment. 'When assessing what is known at present about the kinetics of schoepite [a hydrated oxide of uranium], one realises that more studies must be done to estimate this mineral's solubility as a function of its crystalline state, the local acidity and composition of the soil and the partial pressure of carbonic anhydride. New studies are also desirable on the relationship between contaminated soil and water, with respect to the food chain and human health. This will require studies on plant growth in the presence of schoepite and analyses of the vegetable matter which forms in these soils'.

In their general conclusions, even while these experts downplay the potential dangers, they propose a certain number of precautions, including the periodic monitoring of wells and other sources of drinking water – and even suggest that 'if the uranium concentration goes above the norms set by local authorities, there are two options: either cease to use the wells for drinking water, or treat the water before use, by means of filters that can eliminate the uranium.' A tall order, we might say, especially if we think of the social and economic plight of Iraq. Where does one find 'filters that can eliminate the uranium' in a country subject to embargo? Can they actually 'cease to use the wells for drinking water' in arid regions with few streams?

In conclusion

The DU which remains in metallic form on battlegrounds after projectiles have missed their targets is subject to a slow process of decay and surface oxidation. The projectiles still intact are often buried quite deep in the ground, while their fragments can present a direct risk to the health of local populations, because they may be collected (for use as metal, or for children's games) and kept without any precautions. They are a direct risk for the environment, because the products of decay and oxidation become slowly soluble in water and seep into the deep, damp layers until they eventually reach the groundwater, causing contamination of local wells, streams and ponds. The time-span of this process depends very much on local climatic conditions and on the nature of the soil.

It is harder to assess what happens to the DU that is partly transformed into an aerosol, after projectiles have struck targets or rocks. Dust contaminated by DU and its oxides, which is initially concentrated around the battle sites, can later be spread by the winds over vast areas, so that its concentration may become negligible. But it too can contribute to the contamination of the soil, especially in arid regions, with the same long-term effects as the metallic fragments. In both cases, nothing allows us to rule out the possibility of long-term environmental contamination, as uranium compounds slowly proceed to enter the beginning of the food chain. The current vagueness of scientific knowledge about the essential features of uranium's transformation in the environment – shown in the UNEP report – ought to be sufficient reason for the halting and banning of all further military use of DU (and probably civilian use too).

A final word: our interest in possible and predictable DU contamination should not cause us to forget that every battleground (or, given the strategies apparently favoured by the great powers, every locality destroyed by blind waves of air-strikes) is an endless source of contamination and death, for centuries to come. Early in this chapter we quoted a sentence from the EPI: 'there is no legal requirement to remediate environmental damage to battlefields'. That clarifies the current position of the belligerents – one can destroy, with no 'legal requirement' to decontaminate. The report on the possible consequences of a fire at the Aberdeen base, also quoted above, begins with a long list of chemical products (most being explosives used or substances created at the moment of explosion) and heavy metals (projectile components), of which DU is only a minor component. We cannot forget that every act of war is at the same time an act of war against the environment.

POSTSCRIPTS 2003:
A detailed environmental assessment of depleted uranium has been published by the 'Military Toxics Project'.
(www.miltoxproj.org/assesment.htm)
The long-term question of low radioactivity in the environment is treated in A. Gsponer, J.-P. Hurni, and B. Vitale, 'A comparison of delayed radiobiological effects of depleted uranium munitions versus fourth generation nuclear weapons', Report ISRI-02-07, Proceedings of the 4th Int. Conf. of the Yugoslav Nuclear Society, Belgrade, Sep.30 – Oct.4, 2002, 14 pp. Available at http://arXiv.org/abs/physics/0210071

Chapter 9
Iraq (1991)

During the Gulf War (Operation 'Desert Storm'), the US armed forces used more than 940,000 DU-tipped projectiles with a diameter of 30mm, and more than 14,000 bombs containing DU. This makes a total of at least 315 tonnes of DU, which were left in the region as metal fragments or munitions that missed their targets or – in the case of an estimated 30% to 40% – were transformed into aerosols or dust when they struck Iraqi tanks or the concrete of Iraqi bunkers. The dust (predominantly oxides of uranium) which covers the destroyed tanks and their surroundings is subsequently rendered partly soluble, through the actions of atmospheric phenomena, and filters slowly into the soil (see Chapter 8 'Environmental Effects of DU'). The aerosols are carried by wind and rain far from the battlegrounds.

There are 697,000 US veterans of Desert Storm, and nearly 300,000 of these entered Kuwait and Iraq during the military operations. Several hundred went inside Iraqi tanks destroyed by DU projectiles; others were victims of 'friendly fire' when their tanks were hit by US shells; and thirty of these still carry in their bodies some DU fragments which could not be removed surgically. But more than 100,000 of the veterans later reported serious malaise, chronic fatigue, inability to work etc. – they reported this after returning to the USA, and the cluster of illnesses was labelled 'Gulf War Syndrome' (Zajic 1999, ch.9; Fahey 2000).

Similarly, some of the nearly 50,000 British veterans showed corresponding symptoms and are currently under observation (MoD 1999). The French Ministry of Defence has likewise launched an epidemiological study 'aimed at better assessing the possible health consequences of the French military involvement' (Nau 2001).

It was only in 1994 – three years after the first use of DU weapons in warfare – that the US Congress asked the US Army's Environmental Policy Institute to study 'the health and environmental consequences of using depleted uranium (DU) on the battlefield. The study also examined the potential for remediating DU contamination, ways to reduce DU toxicity, and methods to protect the environment from the long-term consequences of DU use.' (EPI 1994). Among the summary findings we read: 'Radiological Risks Not Completely Understood but Not Underestimated....Toxicological Risks Not Completely Understood... DU may become Mobile in the

Environment'. Nevertheless, this did not prevent the use of these munitions some years later, in Bosnia and Serbia.

Many possible factors have been suggested to account for the illnesses that are conveniently grouped under the label 'Gulf War Syndrome'. These factors have been studied particularly by the RAND Corporation, under contract with the US Department of Defense, (RAND 1999; for DU see Harley et al. 1999). Consideration has been given to the stress suffered by the military personnel, to the many vaccines and other medications they received, to the toxicity of the smoke from burning oil wells, and finally to the possible toxic and radioactive effects of contamination by DU.

The tendency has always been to downplay the seriousness of the symptoms observed, which are often characterised as 'subjective'. However, there are other effects that can be more easily and objectively observed, and should give more reliable results, such as birth deformities in the children of Gulf War veterans. The first available epidemiological data (1997) seemed to deny the existence of observable, statistically significant, effects. In 33,998 children born to a group of 578,705 veterans between 1991 and 1993, 7.1% showed pathological signs at birth and 1.8% had serious deformities; whereas in 41,463 children born to a group of 699,954 US soldiers who had not served in the Gulf War, 7.2 % showed birth defects and 1.8 % serious deformities. These percentages were statistically the same for these two groups and for the general civilian population (Cowan et al., 1997). It was noted, however, that this study covered only the pregnancies that reached full term with normal childbirth, and that a more complete epidemiological study should have taken account of miscarriages and abortions caused by serious congenital malformations of the foetus (Doyle et al., 1997).

More recent studies could indeed cast doubt on at least some of those conclusions. A study done by the Epidemiological and Environmental Service (of the US Veterans Department), and published in the Annals of Epidemiology, surveyed 15,000 Gulf War veterans and 15,000 other soldiers, looking at the frequency of miscarriages, induced abortions, and birth deformities in the children of female veterans and wives of male veterans, in comparison with other female soldiers and veterans' wives. The men and women who had seen action in the Gulf showed 'a significantly higher frequency of miscarriages' and 'significantly more deformities in the children born alive'. The study concludes that: 'the likelihood of soldiers reporting defects in their children correlates significantly with active service in the Gulf War.'

However, the authors are not totally satisfied with their results; they suspect some biases in the data-gathering and recommend a more careful analysis of the medical files (Kang et al., 2001).

(For a more general analysis of the problems posed by DU, see Chapter 6, 'Health effects of DU' and Chapter 8, 'Environmental effects of DU').

All these studies, of course, relate only to Western veterans of the Gulf War, and leave huge question marks about possible negative health effects of DU exposure. Besides, these analyses are only short-term ones, and the populations they relate to, though certainly at risk, were exposed to possible DU contamination for only short periods (with the sole exception of those veterans who still have DU fragments in their bodies).

There have been no careful or long-term studies of the effects on the Iraqi veterans and civilian population, despite the fact that 1,400 of the 3,700 Iraqi tanks destroyed during 'Desert Storm' were struck by DU projectiles (Zajic 1999, ch.6). Furthermore, certain targets – defined as 'military' or 'strategic' by the Allies and as 'civilian refuges' by the Iraqis, (the Baghdad bunker, for example) – may have been chosen as 'high-priority targets' for testing prototypes of DU bombs (IDUST 2001). And of course a large proportion of Iraq's population has, for years, been inhaling dust and drinking water polluted by DU.

One must also bear in mind that in matters of sanitation, medical monitoring and pharmaceutical care, the situation of Western veterans cannot be compared to that of the Iraqi population. The Iraqi people today are a group rendered fragile by years of malnutrition, chronic poverty and inadequate medical care. Any attack on the immune system of people (especially children) living in such conditions, whether due to DU pollution or other chemical pollution caused by the war, can only exacerbate and multiply the adverse effects of every environmental degradation, including the presence of DU.

The documents and testimonies presented at the 'Conference on the Health and Environmental Consequences of DU used by US and British Forces during the 1991 Gulf War' give cause for concern and merit close study, (Lopez 1998: see Mould 2001 for a critical analysis of the cancer statistics presented at this conference). The same applies to the direct testimonies of Robert Fisk (Fisk 1998). The epidemiological situation described in the international conference on 'Depleted Uranium: health, legal and economic aspects of the use of radioactive weapons', which relates to the incidence of cancers and deformities in the Basra region (southern Iraq, near the combat region) is also troubling (Yacoup et al. 2000).

There may be reason for doubts and reservations about the statistical validity of these studies and the methodology used (Mould 2001). But these doubts only highlight the urgency of setting up a large international study that would cover the different regions of Iraq and try to account for the possible causes of cancers and deformities (chemical pollution, the destruction of oil wells, malnutrition, etc.) found in a population that has been malnourished and weakened by years of sanctions.

It is only quite recently that the WHO saw fit to show interest in the consequences of DU pollution in Iraq. In a statement of 15 September 2001, the WHO announced that a delegation of experts had returned from Iraq and proposed four research projects to be conducted in collaboration with Iraqi scientists: 'a detailed statistical analysis of cancer cases and congenital deformities; a similar analysis of renal illnesses; a study of the options for monitoring cancers and other non-infectious diseases; a study of the possible pathogenic effects on health of environmental factors such as DU.' We are now awaiting the first results of these studies. But obviously the difficulties caused by the US-backed sanctions very much decrease the opportunities for Iraqi professionals to work in the affected regions on the epidemiology of illnesses, deformities and malaises attributed to DU pollution in Iraq. It is possible to assist them by organising shipments of scientific equipment (in particular gamma spectrometers) and up-to-date bibliographic information (Al-Jibouri 2001).

Chapter 10
Bosnia (1995-1996)

NATO estimates that about 11,000 DU projectiles – penetrators 30mm in diameter – were used by the US A-10 aircraft against Serb tanks, military bases and munitions depots in Bosnia in 1994 and 1995 (DoD-NT 2001). The first interventions took place in August and September 1994, in the context of 'Operation Deny Flight' – the two places struck by 980 projectiles (about 300kg of DU) were in the 20-kilometre 'exclusion zone' around Sarajevo. The other interventions occurred in August and September 1995, as part of 'Operation Deliberate Force' – during 17 strikes, more than 10,000 rounds were used, which means about 3 tonnes of DU (NATO-B 2001; NATO-D 2001).

It was not until six years later that NATO admitted having used DU in Bosnia. The first details were supplied on 24 January 2001, when NATO published a list of map coordinates corresponding to the 19 localities struck by DU projectiles (NATO-I 2001). For 13 of these localities they give the number of projectiles used; but for six they say 'unknown', which seems strange in view of the bureaucratic precision of military arsenals. A map identifying the areas struck in September 1995 was published on 31 January 2001 (NATO -BI, 2001).

It is hard to evaluate the long-term danger posed by over 3 tonnes of DU in Bosnia. As we outlined in Chapter 5, 'The Behaviour of Uranium in the Human Body', the health and environmental dangers of DU, as well as the urgency of decontaminating the polluted areas, depend very much on the nature of the contamination. The penetrators that missed their targets and now lie buried in the ground, plus the fragments of metallic DU remaining on the surface, undergo a slow process of oxidation which means that later these DU compounds seep into the groundwater and enter the food chain. Meanwhile, the portion of the DU that changed into aerosol on impact settles as a fine dust on the site and later, carried by wind and rain, contributes to the contamination of the surrounding population when they inhale or ingest it.

The percentage of penetrators which hit their targets cannot be calculated precisely. No experimental data can be found for Bosnia. We can only extrapolate from data gathered by UNEP in Kosovo, data which we will discuss further in the next chapter (UNEP 2001). After visiting eleven of the sites where NATO admitted using these projectiles, the UNEP team found only 7 penetrators (and one fragment) out of about 31,000 DU rounds used in the 1999 air-strikes over Yugoslavia – and these were found in only five of the eleven sites explored. This might mean that most of them hit their targets, in which case the amount of aerosol released into the environment is enormous and may constitute a serious and immediate danger to human health. Alternatively, it may be that many projectiles missed and remain in the ground, in which case one must fear long-term environmental contamination (of the earth, the groundwater and the local surface water).

If we can trust the information coming from Bratunac (in Republika Srpska which, alongside the Bosniak-Croat Federation, forms the Bosnia of today), then at least some of the DU projectiles used in the 1994 campaign struck an inhabited region, 'Serbian Sarajevo' – in other words the Hadzici district on the outskirts of Sarajevo. NATO suspected at that time that Radovan Karadzic was hiding there. The entire Serbian population of Hadzici took refuge, after the Dayton Accords of November 1995, in the Bosnian-Serb village of Bratunac. Jela Jovanovic has reported that in the Bratunac population originating from Hadzici, deaths were much higher than births, and cancer cases were five times more numerous than in the natives of Bratunac. She has the impression also that a similar situation exists in many Bosnian-Serb villages in people who had fled Sarajevo and its environs and taken refuge in the Serbian Republic of Bosnia (Jovanovic 2001). Equally alarming reports have come from the Kasin Dol Hospital, near Sarajevo (Sito-Sucic 2001; Zuza 2001). Given that cancer takes time to kill, one would expect that many deaths resulting from exposure to carcinogens in 1994 would not occur until after 1998.

Unfortunately the political authorities in Bosnia seem at present very uninterested in paying attention to this problem and carefully finding the facts. So far there has been no epidemiological analysis done in the places where NATO admits using DU, or in the villages where the populations in question now reside – i.e. to which the inhabitants of areas where DU was used, shifted or were shifted after the fighting.

Can we speak here of political and diplomatic reasons – a reluctance on the part of the Bosnian authorities to embarrass the masters of NATO or to jeopardise the funds promised for reconstruction?

POSTSCRIPT 2003: a report dated 2 May 2002 on the health of Romanian veterans who had served in Bosnia is availible at: www.accessatlanta.com/ajc/news/0502/03gulfvets.html

Chapter 11
Serbia (including Kosovo) 1999

Beginning on 24 March 1999, NATO aircraft bombarded Yugoslavia for 78 days. In particular, US A-10 aircraft used at least 30,000 DU rounds against Serbian tanks, in other words more than 9 tonnes of DU.

It was not easy to gain confirmation that DU was present in some of the projectiles used by the A-10s in the Kosovo War, because these aircraft can also shoot high explosive incendiary rounds (HEIs). After the massive use of DU in the Gulf War there were strong suspicions that the same scenario was being enacted against Serbia. The BBC correspondent Alex Kirby discussed and denounced this use of DU as early as 9 April 1999 (Kirby, 1999). But no official confirmation emerged from NATO.

Some altogether paradoxical situations resulted. For example, the experts from the UN Environment Programme (UNEP), in their first report on the possible health and environmental effects of the use of DU weaponry in Kosovo (October 1999), were forced to admit that: 'there is no official document confirming or denying that DU was used in Kosovo; consequently, we have received no information about the sites where it was used or how it was used.' (UNEP 1999). This was not an ideal starting point for their fieldwork and demarcation of contaminated sites.

A year passed before NATO acknowledged officially that it had used DU in the Kosovo War. On 7 February 2000 the Secretary-General of NATO, Lord Robertson, wrote in a letter to his UN counterpart Kofi Annan:

DU rounds were used whenever the A-10 engaged armour during Operation Allied Force. Therefore, it was used throughout Kosovo during approximately 100 missions. The GAU-8/A API round is designated PGU-13/B and uses a streamlined projectile housing a sub-calibre kinetic energy penetrator machined from DU ... A total of approximately 31,000 rounds of DU ammunition was used in operation Allied Force. The major focus of these operations was in an area west of the Pec-Dakovica-Prizren highway, in the area surrounding Klina, in the area around Prizren and in an area to the north of a line joining Suva Reka and Urosevac. However, many missions using DU also took place outside these areas. At this moment it is impossible to state accurately every location where DU ammunition was used (WISE 2001: 'Current issues; Depleted uranium weapons; Depleted uranium use in Kosovo').

On 24 January 2001, NATO published a list of map coordinates corresponding to the 96 localities struck by DU projectiles during 112 attacks (85 in Kosovo, 10 in Serbia, 1 in Montenegro); for 23 attacks the number of DU rounds used is stated as 'unknown' (NATO-Ia, 2001). As in the case of Bosnia (see the previous chapter), this is rather strange, considering the bureaucratic precision of military arsenals. A map identifying the areas struck between 6 April and 10 June 1999 was published subsequently, on 31 January 2001 (NATO-BI, 2001).

It is still not clear whether other DU weapons were used against Yugoslavia, apart from those penetrators fired from the A-10 aircraft. Jane's, the famous organisation that analyses military systems, seems to suspect so or to consider it possible: 'It is true that certain types of guided missile use DU to increase their penetrating power, and that the Phalanx system, which is used to protect warships from surface missiles, also plans to use DU munitions' (Jane's 2001).

What made it possible eventually to obtain official information and confirmations about the presence of DU in the Balkans after its use in Bosnia and Serbia (including Kosovo) was the fact that a syndrome appeared among the veterans of the NATO actions – the 'Balkans Syndrome', which recalls the 'Gulf War Syndrome' that had afflicted the veterans of 1991.

After the Gulf War, there were very serious impacts on the health of the Iraqi population attributed to DU – cancers, birth deformities, miscarriages, etc. – but which do not seem to have troubled what is called the 'international community' (see Chapter 9 'Iraq'). It was only after the western veterans complained of malaise, incomprehensible fatigue, memory disturbances etc. that people started speaking of the 'Gulf War Syndrome' and suspecting that DU was at least partly to blame.

The same scenario was played out with the Balkans. Reports drawing attention to serious impacts on the health of Bosnian and Serbian populations did not move NATO. Nobody spoke of a 'Balkans Syndrome' until the evidence emerged, from January 2001 onwards, of a statistically abnormal number of leukaemia cases among the soldiers in KFOR (notably Italian, Portuguese and Spanish soldiers: see for example Castañón Blanco 2001). That report caused some agitation in the military forces and in the international organisations which are supposed to be concerned with the health of populations.

The British Minister of Defence sent a mission to Kosovo in January 2001 'in response to the concerns expressed by the veterans about the possible risks posed by the DU munitions used by NATO in the Balkans' (MoD-MP 2001). Although this report tries on the whole to be reassuring, at least for the British veterans (the experts explored only the part of Kosovo where UK soldiers were stationed), people may be less reassured by some of its findings: the unexpected presence of gamma rays caused by the decay of radioactive caesium (C_s137), some localised spots of high-intensity alpha radiation caused by DU, and a large number of penetrators which had missed their targets ('some hundreds of rounds are used in every air-strike, and a significant portion of these arrows penetrate the ground around the target [after missing it]'. These remain buried up to five metres underground, thus escaping detection by all the means usually employed.

The UN Environmental Programme (UNEP) also published a report, which was based on a visit to Kosovo by its experts from 5 to 19 November 2001 – we mentioned this in our previous chapter (UNEP 2001; see Busby's criticisms of this report, Busby 2001). Here again the conclusions seek to be reassuring: 'No detectable large-scale contamination was found [...] Detectable contamination due to DU is limited to localised points close to penetrator impact sites or penetrator holes [...] No contamination was found in water, in milk, in objects or in buildings'. Nevertheless, 'It is probable that many penetrators are hidden several metres below ground level. These penetrators, like those on the surface, constitute a risk of future DU contamination of groundwater and drinking water [...] The radiation doses will be very low but the resulting uranium concentration might exceed WHO health standards for drinking water.'

The report published later by the US Department of Defense attempts likewise to reassure. Its general conclusions include these words: 'The medical and environmental assessments and investigations made by the various countries, international organizations, and private groups have had generally similar results. None have found a connection between DU exposure and leukaemia or other medical problems in people, and none have found widespread DU contamination sufficient to impact the health of the general population or deployed military personnel [of KFOR].' (DoD-IP 2001).

Now it is clear that in Serbia, as in Iraq, the extent of chemical pollution caused by the war is greater and more serious than that caused by DU alone (Nasy 1999 provides a long list of chemical plants and depots destroyed by the NATO bombardments of Serbia). And this chemical pollution may have contributed, at least partly, to the difficult health situation reported in Bosnia and Serbia. Unfortunately, we have to repeat now what we said in our chapter about Bosnia: that the government – here the Serbian government – is showing a total lack of zeal about ascertaining or monitoring the serious health problems which are reported by its citizens and attributed, at least in part, to DU in the environment (see for example Mara et al., 1999, BBC 2001). As in Bosnia, no large-scale epidemiological study has been done in the Serbian localities where DU was used. Here too, we may ask whether political or diplomatic reasons are involved, a reluctance to embarrass the masters of NATO (which caused the destruction) and thereby lose the funds promised for reconstruction.

The fact that KFOR, which operates in Kosovo under NATO mandate, is even less zealous (if that is possible) about studying the effects of the probable DU contamination reported by UNEP in the region's soil and groundwater is, naturally, far easier to understand.

NOTE

An account (in Italian) of a visit to Kosovo in September 1999 to study possible DU contamination and its effects (Mara et al. 1999) may be requested from its authors:

Luigi Mara, Bruno Theme e Marco Caldirola : Indagine in Kosovo sull'inquinamento da uranio impoverito. Milano : Medicina Democratica e Centro Regionale di Intervento per la Cooperazione, settembre 1999.

Medicina Democratica, via Venezian 1 – I-20133 Milano (medicinademocratica@liberto.it)

POSTSCRIPT 2003: A technical paper, T.E.Liolios: 'Assessing the risk from the depleted uranium weapons used in Operation Allied Force' may be seen at http://arXiv:physics/9904061

Chapter 12

Okinawa, Panama, Vieques, and Other US Bases around the World

The military bases operated by the USA, both at home and abroad, are garbage-heaps of dangerous chemicals and unexploded munitions (Kovaleski 1998). This is particularly true of those where new weapons are tested (see Williams et al. 1998 for an impressive list of chemicals – including DU – which in the case of fire could cause serious health problems around the weapons testing site at Aberdeen, Maryland).

One of the causes of contamination of testing sites was the trial use of DU weapons. On just one of them, the Jefferson Proving Ground, in Indiana, the following is reported:

> From 1984 to 1994, the licensee conducted accuracy testing of depleted Uranium (DU) tank penetrator rounds at the site ... The DU munitions testing contaminated approximately 5,100,000 square meters (1,260 acres) on the site with an estimated 70,000 kg of DU ... Currently, the licensed material is kept onsite in the restricted area known as 'Depleted Uranium Impact Area'. This area ... is located north of the firing line, and consists of approximately 12,000,000 square meters (3000 acres) (FR 1999).

The presence within the United States of testing-sites for DU weapons provokes strong reactions from local communities (see for example RAMA 2000). But of course the situation in and around US testing-grounds abroad is even more worrying, in view of the relative weakness of local communities and often even local governments compared with the power of the US. These bases and testing-grounds are very numerous, and they are found in almost all parts of the planet.

We will give here some information about the health and environment problems which some of these bases create for local populations and surrounding areas, in the specific case of the presence of DU munitions. This cannot, however, be a comprehensive list – there are certainly many cases we do not know about and which the international media have not mentioned.

1. Okinawa (Japan, the US military base at Camp Schwab, Torishima)

The US Government never notified the Japanese Government of its desire to test DU projectiles stored at this base. It was only on 10 February 1997 that the Pentagon officially acknowledged that a test had been conducted, in the autumn of 1995, in which a Harrier aircraft of the US Navy had fired 1520 DU rounds, containing a total of 251kg of DU; no measures were taken subsequently to retrieve whatever penetrators might have remained on the island of Torishima. In the wake of this incident and the reactions of the local population and Japanese Government, the Pentagon announced that all the DU munitions stored at Okinawa had been transferred to South Korea (Catalinotto et al. 2000).

2. Panama (US military bases at Balboa West and Pinas, plus the New Empire Range testing-ground – all occupied until 31 December 1999)
These three bases covered more than 10,000 hectares, mostly comprising rain forest; about a third of this area was used solely as a shooting range, ever since the First World War, and consequently it is literally littered with all sorts of munitions fragments and unexploded projectiles. When the US occupation of the Canal Zone ended (31 December 1999), the US Government had undertaken – in the Panama Canal Treaty of 1977 – to return these areas free from all contamination and to provide the Panamanian authorities with all the data they needed about the activities of the bases and the levels of contamination. It seems that now the US military has declared that total decontamination is impossible, for technical reasons, and is even dangerous for water quality in the region of the canal ('the canal watershed', Kovaleski 1998).

Precise information about DU weapons testing at the Panama bases is very hard to obtain, because the US military authorities have endeavoured to hide all evidence of the very presence of such munitions on Panamanian soil. Rick Stauber, a former de-mining expert of the US Department of Defense, who undertook a report in 1996 about the contamination of bases in Panama, declares that DU munitions with a diameter of 120mm were tested at the New Empire Range on at least three occasions between 1983 and 1985 (Lindsay-Poland 1997, Mitchell 1997; the source of these dates is Cajar Páez 2001). At first the US authorities denied this information, but they admitted later that DU projectiles had been stored (only temporarily) at the Panama bases in order 'to test their deterioration in tropical climates', declaring also that they had been taken back to the USA afterwards. Stauber insisted that his account was correct, noting that the military authorities would have test-fired at least some of these projectiles to assess whether they remained functional (Catalinotto et al. 2000).

On the eve of the transfer of the Canal Zone into Panamanian hands, these areas were still covered with munitions debris and the remains of chemical weapons storage areas. The testing-grounds are now surrounded by barbed wire, with warnings posted at intervals saying: 'Explosives Kill. No Entry.' Yet more than 20,000 small farmers live in the surrounding districts, and they often enter these areas to gather metal fragments, to fish, or to cultivate the abandoned terrain. (Kovaleski 1998)

3. Puerto Rico (the island of Vieques)

Vieques is a little island 31km long and 7km wide situated off the east coast of the main island of Puerto Rico. It has about 10,000 inhabitants. Since 1940, half the island and the surrounding ocean has been used by the US Navy as a testing-site. This is where the US Navy prepared for all its most important actions since the Korean War, and where the military tested all sorts of weapons, including the napalm used in the Vietnam War.

The debate about the presence of DU on the island arose from an official navy bulletin of 5 March 2000 which reported that on 19 February 1999 two naval aircraft had fired 263 DU projectiles in the North Convoy area on Vieques. The context was a technical evaluation exercise for the Phalanx naval defence system, and allegedly these projectiles had been fired in error (US Navy 2000).

The US Nuclear Regulatory Commission (NCR) then studied the Navy's plans in order to retrieve the penetrators of these projectiles (each penetrator weighs about 300g). By 30 June 2000, 37 of these had been retrieved, leaving 226 penetrators unaccounted for, which amounts to over 65kg of DU – and it was not known whether they had fallen in the sea or buried themselves deep into the ground (WISE 2001: 'Current Issues, Depleted Uranium Weapons; Inadvertent DU Ammunition Use by US Navy in Vieques, Puerto Rico'; see our chapter 5: 'The Behaviour of DU in the Human Body' for what happens to buried fragments of metallic DU). It was announced later, on 27 November 2000, that 57 penetrators had been retrieved, but that no trace had been found of the other 206 (Catalinotto et al. 2000).

Even before this episode, however, there had been uneasiness about the health problems which the inhabitants of Vieques were reporting. In the 1990s, between the Gulf War and the Kosovo War, all kinds of bombs had been exploded on the Vieques testing-ground. According to a study from the Puerto Rico Department of Health, the cancer rate on Vieques is 27% higher than in the rest of Puerto Rico. Dr Rafael Rivera Castaño, who lives on Vieques, claims that the rate has increased recently, reaching 52% above the general average (quoted by Ruiz Marrero 2001).

Cruz M. Nazario Delgado, a professor in the University of Puerto Rico's Department of Biostatistics and Epidemiology, has written a very serious report about health on Vieques; and she tells us 'I have no proofs about [links between] cancer deaths and uranium levels on Vieques, since the real problem is the fact that the laboratories don't want to give us their results, or claim not to have any standard data with which the patients' [urine] samples can be compared. There is no doubt that the US military on Vieques has used a great deal more DU munitions that it says it has' (Nazario-Delgado 2001). A similar assessment is made by Carmelo Ruiz-Marrero, of the Common Dreams News Center (Ruiz-Marrero 2001; see also Red Betances 2001 and Wilcox 2001).

There is obvious contamination of the island's earth and air, leading to a much higher morbidity in the local people than in the rest of Puerto Rico's population. In the soil of Vieques, including its groundwater, and in its ocean, very high concentrations of numerous toxic substances are found (aromatic polycyclics like RDX and HMX, toluidine, cyanide, heavy metals...). In view of the likely multiple causes of the chemical contamination reported on Vieques, it is difficult to know whether the US Navy lied or not when it claimed that only one episode of DU use occurred in the island's history, or whether there are so many other toxic substances present that the role of DU can only be marginal. After the mobilisation of the island's population, the US Navy withdrew from Vieques on 1 May 2000, although demands for them to clean up the island continue.

Chapter 13

International Laws and Conventions on the Use of Depleted Uranium

General Sir Hugh Beach was the man who ordered research in Britain into the development of DU weapons. In his report 'The Military Hazards of Depleted Uranium', he wrote:

> 'Like other heavy metals (mercury or lead) uranium in soluble form is toxic. This means that once dissolved in the blood in sufficient quantity it can cause damage to body tissue, particularly the kidneys, leading to health problems. About 90% of soluble uranium is excreted in the urine within 48 hours. The remaining 10% retained in the body could lead to long-term health effects, chronic kidney damage being the most probable.' (Beach 2001)

Once he had explained 'the military usefulness of DU' and the kinds of 'DU-based munitions in action', General Beach discussed the 'radiation hazards from military possession of DU' and the 'radiation hazards from the use of DU-based ammunition in action'. He stated that:

> '...much of the radioactive aerosol outside the target vehicle [when hit by a DU missile] is carried up on a column of hot air created by the heat of the explosion... Tests in England have shown that radioactive material is difficult to detect more than about 100 metres from the target even with the best monitoring equipment. It must be admitted however that there is a lack of useful published experimental data to support this finding.' (Beach 2001)

General Beach continued with 'the hazard from chemical toxicity due to the use of DU in action'. In particular, he remarked:

> 'The real reason for concern ... lies in the clouds of uranium dust thrown up by the impact of DU penetrators on hard objects such as tanks... Uranium, in the form of the uranyl ion, can react with other biological molecules (bicarbonates, citrates, phosphates, proteins, etc.) causing damage (to the body).'

These statements are consistent with the information and analysis discussed in Ch. 6: The Effects of DU on Health. In light of this information, the following clear-cut statement is surprising:

'The British government has stated categorically that in its opinion use of

DU ammunition is not proscribed by the Geneva protocols nor by any other international agreement to which the UK is a party' (Beach 2001).

So what are these agreements, and more specifically, these protocols? The Geneva Convention (1949) was modified by two protocols during a 'Diplomatic Conference on International Humanitarian Law Applicable in Armed Conflicts' (1977). These protocols restrict the right of warring parties to choose weapons and methods 'of a nature to cause superfluous injury or unnecessary suffering' or which may be expected to cause 'widespread, long-term and severe damage to the natural environment'.

Interestingly, although these two protocols have not been ratified by the USA, Great Britain has ratified them (Roberts et al. 2000; see also Goldblat 1996). Despite this, the British government does not consider that using DU weapons violates these protocols.

In 1996, the United Nations Sub-Commission on the Promotion and Protection of Human Rights (a sub commission of the UN Commission on Human Rights) passed a resolution (96/16) condemning the use of all 'weapons of mass destruction *or* with indiscriminate effect, in particular nuclear weapons, chemical weapons, fuel-air bombs, napalm, cluster bombs, biological weaponry and weaponry containing depleted uranium'. Note that the 'or' in this sentence has been used to show that in the Sub-Commission's opinion, DU weapons are not necessarily included in the definition 'weapons of mass destruction' (a category which, according to some interpretations, should only include nuclear weapons). However, DU weapons are included explicitly with the weapons whose use is condemned due to their 'indiscriminate effects'.

According to General Beach, DU weapons could even be classed as radiological weapons. But, he adds, 'there is no international instrument forbidding the use or possession of radiological weapons'. It seems that a 1979 proposal by the United States and the Soviet Union to ban weapons that are *specifically designed* to employ radioactive material by disseminating it to cause destruction, damage or injury by means of the radioactive decay of such material' was never accepted at an international level.

Could they at least be considered 'chemical weapons', because of the toxicity of uranium? Not according to General Beach. The Chemical Weapons Convention (1993, ratified by the USA, Russia, and all members of NATO, came into force in 1998) and defines 'chemical weapons' as all weapons or other objects 'specifically designed to cause death or other harm through the toxic properties of those chemicals'. Although DU is chemically toxic, DU weapons are not 'specifically designed' to cause death or other harm because of their toxicity, but through their penetrating power. Therefore, 'DU-based ammunition is not a chemical weapon within the terms of the Chemical Weapons Convention'.

Could they at least be considered 'incendiary weapons', given the tendency of uranium to ignite as a result of violent shocks with solid objects such as armour-plated tanks and cement fortifications around bunkers? Not according to General Beach. Once again, it is a question of semantic detail. While the Convention on Prohibitions or Restrictions on the use of Certain Conventional Weapons (1980, ratified by the USA and Great Britain) prohibits attacks on civilians and forests with air-delivered incendiary weapons, it does not protect combatants against these weapons. Worse still, it does not clearly differentiate between weapons which have been 'specifically designed' to ignite fires and other weapons 'in which the incendiary effect is incidental' but does not necessarily occur.

General Beach concluded: 'Nevertheless the fact that DU poses all three types of hazard (radioactive, toxicity and incendiary) means that it deserves special attention.' That is as far as he goes.

These subtle legal distinctions which are conveniently blurry in international conventions (and if they are not blurry enough, nations refuse to sign them), have been used by the International Criminal Tribunal for the former Yugoslavia (ICTY) to acquit NATO of any sanction for having used DU weapons during the wars in Bosnia and Kosovo. In fact, the commission charged by the ICTY with assessing NATO's bombing campaign against the Federal Republic of Yugoslavia decided in its final report that:

'In view of the uncertain state of development of the legal standards governing this area, it should be emphasised that the use of depleted uranium or other potentially hazardous substance by any adversary to conflicts within the former Yugoslavia since 1991 has not formed the basis of any charge laid by the Prosecutor ... It is therefore the opinion of the committee, based on information available at present, that the OTP (Office of the Prosecutor) should not commence an investigation into use of depleted uranium projectiles by NATO.' (ICTY 2000)

Legal expert Karen Parker (Euler et al. 1999; HLP 1997 2001; HRIN 2001; Parker 2000) holds a totally different opinion. She has presented her findings to the UN Commissioner for Human Rights

on several occasions. Her case can be summarised as follows:
There are four rules derived from the whole of humanitarian law regarding military conduct and weapons:

(1) Weapons may only be used in the legal field of battle, defined as legal military targets of the enemy in the war. Weapons may not have an adverse effect off the legal field of battle. (The 'territorial' test).

(2) Weapons can only be used for the duration of an armed conflict. A weapon that is used or continues to act after the war is over violates this criterion. (The 'temporal' test).

(3) Weapons may not be unduly inhumane. (The 'humaneness' test).

(4) Weapons may not have an unduly negative effect on the natural environment. (The 'environmental' test).

In Karen Parker's opinion, DU weaponry fails all four tests. The effects of DU weapons cannot be restricted to the battlefield, but risk spreading to much larger areas (thus failing the territorial test). Their effects remain much longer than the duration of hostilities (failing the temporal test). The effects on the human body, particularly among civilians after the hostilities are over, can be very serious (failing the humaneness test). Finally, DU weaponry cannot be used without unduly damaging the natural environment (failing the environmental test).

Those opposing Karen Parker have pointed out that there is no international convention which explicitly prohibits the use of DU weaponry. General Beach's arguments have been outlined above. However, as Karen Parker explains in her publications and submissions to the United Nations, the 'laws and customs of war' do not only consist of the international treaties, conventions and agreements ratified by a few countries. Treaties such as these obviously constrain only the states that have signed them. But, if a military practice (in particular, the use of certain types of weapons) violates the 'laws and customs of war' this practice (the use of this type of weaponry) is illegal for all states whether or not they have ratified particular agreements (Parker 2000).

Of course, it could be asked whether these issues of international jurisprudence are relevant when mobilising public opinion against DU weapons. Treaties, conventions and agreements between states have always been limited by compromise, individual interests and the political strategies of the states which sign them. States often sign these agreements for tactical reasons when they are being formulated, but do not ratify them later. In other cases states fail to respect agreements even after ratifying them.

110

So many officially illegal acts are carried out by all the world's great powers with total immunity, for example: the US irradiation experiments on the civilian population without their knowledge (ACHRE 1997); the distribution of millions of kilograms of dioxin-containing defoliant (agent orange) during the Vietnam war (Jaeggi 2000); and acts of sabotage and arming the 'contras' in Nicaragua. All these examples could lead to the slightly cynical position that the legal avenues are not very useful and that other forms of action are necessary. However, there is certainly a place for legal opinions, especially in a world where the great powers claim to be the guardians of democracy, freedom, and respect for human rights. Helping to unmask the great powers will surely open them up to wider criticism and convince a larger audience of the truth.

Conclusion to the 'Open-ended' Chapters

In a January 2001 press release, NATO solemnly declared:

> 'The Allies [in this case NATO] are committed to ensuring the health and safety of their servicemen and servicewomen and to avoiding any ill-effects for the civilian population and the personnel of non-governmental organisations as a result of NATO military operations' (NATO- IB 2001).

The evidence presented in the preceding chapters proves that this statement is a lie. The 'Allies' of the Gulf War (officially the United Nations) as well as the 'Allies' of the Balkan War (NATO) created potentially dangerous situations for the local populations and the environment. The most basic 'precautionary principle' would have stopped any deployment of DU weapons right from the beginning, given that the toxic and radioactive properties of U-238 had been known for a long time. It was also obvious that the complicated chemistry of uranium and the very long half-life of U-238 make it highly unlikely that decontamination could be achieved.

Wherever possible we have used the 'hostile witness' method which is well known to readers of US crime novels. That is, we have tried to quote from defence ministries' official documents, military press releases and reports of official institutions (often biased towards the power structures) so as to reveal the true scenario which contradicts the NATO statement cited above. Thus, we have shown that during the development and use of DU, in weapons and for some non-military uses, the significant and predictable risks have been consciously ignored.

Knowingly, and very cynically, the leaders of the great powers decided to give priority to their military strike capability at the expense of the health and the long-term living conditions of the civilian populations that might be attacked. The great powers made that decision with impunity – an impunity of which they are perfectly aware. As long ago as 1994, for example, the 'Report to Congress on Health and Environmental Consequences of Depleted Uranium Use by the US Army' declared:

> 'If providing soldiers in action with weapons that maximise their advantages means that we must use DU, then we must use methods that minimize its potential health and environmental consequences. It is worth

112

noting that, according to current international law, there is no legal obligation to repair environmental damage to a battlefield. Furthermore, it is unlikely that it will become obligatory in future to repair environmental damage to a battlefield solely to eliminate DU.' (EPI 1994).

It would be naïve for anyone to be astonished – on learning about DU – by the cynicism and impunity of the powerful nations and their military leadership. Sixty years of brutal initiatives by the USA alone show a continuous chain of interventions which had serious and long-term effects on civilian populations. Here are some of them: the dropping of the first uranium bomb, on Hiroshima; the dropping of the first plutonium bomb, on Nagasaki; the massive use of napalm and defoliants in the Vietnam War; the intensive production, marketing, and systematic use of land-mines and fragmentation bombs, etc. – right up to the recent bombing campaign in Afghanistan, which used 'bunker-busters' possibly containing DU (the official term for the penetrating substance in these bombs is 'dense metal', which may denote tungsten or may equally well be a euphemism for DU).

The deployment of DU weapons is therefore only one more link in this chain. And it is fair to ask whether the essential goal of these interventions is purely military, as we are told, or whether it includes, alongside the desire for victory with 'zero casualties', the intention of terrorising civilian populations and making their lives impossible for long periods across large regions, and thus preventing them from retaliating. As for the attempts at non-military use of DU, these have been driven not by any social purpose but by the need to reduce dangerous and troublesome stocks of nuclear materials.

Because of this, we think that the campaign against military and civilian uses of DU should not focus exclusively on the dangers of DU, but should be conducted in the more general context of resistance to the great powers' military and economic policies. In this book we have tried to clarify the issues in the DU campaign, which draw on a whole range of technical and interdisciplinary fields of knowledge. This work demands great rigour in data and communication, and seems to require a long collective effort, to be organised on an international scale.

The need to be ready to react and disseminate adequate counter-information is apparent when we read the report of a committee of experts ('a team of lawyers and military experts') which was appointed by the International Criminal Tribunal for former

Yugoslavia (ICTY) to inquire into possible war crimes committed by NATO during the Balkans War. Regarding DU in particular, these 'experts' conclude: 'There is no specific treaty ban on the use of DU projectiles ... It is therefore the opinion of the committee, based on information available at present, that the Office of the Criminal Tribunal should not commence an investigation into use of depleted uranium projectiles by NATO.' This report did not evoke from the media the reactions that it deserved; the people who work, all over the world, to create a tide of public opposition to DU do not seem able to intervene effectively whenever they should.

There is no reason to believe that waiting will solve the problem – it is more likely to worsen it. Every year tens of thousands of tons of DU are added to the existing stocks, increasing the pressure for it to be used more widely, in military and non-military ways. There are many reasons for this state of affairs.

Military spokesmen, in particular, never stop praising the wonders wrought by DU, as the RAND report indicates: 'In conclusion, the use of DU munitions and armor is likely to expand greatly over the coming years, both in the US military and in other countries.' (Harley et al. 1999).

The military-industrial complex, for its part, cannot fail to be interested in new opportunities for products based on an ingredient (DU) that is cheap and widely available – products for which the armed forces provide a guaranteed sale. A likely consequence is that the workers may consider themselves materially interested and may be obliged, under pressure from unemployment or reduced work, to participate in making instruments that can destroy or poison whole populations.

But it would be impossible for the military to enlarge their panoply of death-weapons or the industrialists to increase their production unless the scientists were actively involved in inventing them. This aspect of the problem is almost always forgotten; public confidence in the 'liberating' value or the 'progressive nature' of science (as an organised body of verifiable knowledge) and of scientific institutions (research bodies directed by scientists) is still so strong that it discourages criticism of this essential part of our societies' power structures, and means that the critiques which do appear are cautious, hesitant, and few.

So what can we do about it?

The first obvious action is to acquire and disseminate information, through all the channels of our 'communication society'. Our

114

information must be accurate, targeted, not over-dramatised, not irritating to people who have not made up their minds – and it should not hide those things in our material that are dubious, incompletely understood, and provisional. That is why this book speaks of 'open-ended themes': points on which analysis must continue and, where possible, use new, more reliable, data.

Other actions have been suggested and implemented: arranging national and international meetings; publishing lists of industrial firms making DU products (military or civilian), in preparation for boycott campaigns; lobbying for the establishment of serious decontamination projects and epidemiological studies in Iraq and the Balkans by international bodies like the WHO, UNEP, the US Military and NATO.

Given the current huge imbalance between the great powers and those individuals, organisations and peoples who oppose their projects, it is hard to imagine how the means and objectives of the military leaders can be confronted directly. Obviously a world campaign to eliminate DU from all countries' military arsenals would begin to do this. But there are other possible areas of action: trade unions first of all, where the message could be taken to all workers engaged in building DU products (military or civilian); consumers' organisations, where we might propose boycotts of culpable products or industries; universities and research centres carrying on the primary activity that leads to new weapons and new products, where students and teachers might join in a process of critical reflection about research activities.

In conclusion, we hope that this book will help in the construction of useful tools for future campaigns for information-gathering, information-sharing and effective action.

References to Part II

Abdelkrim-Delanne, Ch.: *Le 'j'accuse' d'un soldat de la guerre du Golfe*. L'Humanité, 16 June 2000.

ACHRE: *Final report, Advisory Committee on Human Radiation Experiments*. Oxford: Oxford University Press, 1997. (http://tis.eh.doe.gov/ohre/roadmap/achre/report.html)

AGWVA-BB: Bulletin-board; *Depleted Uranium hazards in the Gulf War*. Washington: American Gulf War Veterans Association, May 14, 2001. (www.gulfwarvets.com).

AIEA: *Depleted Uranium*. International Atomic Energy Agency, Vienna, 2001. (www.iaea.org).

Al-Jibouri, Mona Kammas: Private communication. Baghdad: Commission on depleted uranium, Ministry of Health, May 19, 2001.

Arkin, W.: *The desert glows – with propaganda*. Bulletin of Atomic Scientists, May 1993.

BBC: *Civilians contaminated by depleted uranium*. BBC 2, Scotland, April 12, 2001.

Barrillot, B.: Munitions à l'uranium appauvri; *La nouvelle artillerie des puissances nucléaires*, in Barrillot et al, 2001, pp.71-86.

Barrillot, B., Castanier, C., Chareyron, B., De Brouwer, Ch., Mampaey, L., Richard, C. M. et Tavitian, N.: *Les armes à uranium appauvri ; Jalons pour une interdiction*. Bruxelles: GRIP, 2001.

Beach, H. (General Sir): *The military hazards of depleted Uranium*. International Security Information Service (ISIS), Briefing Paper no.78, January 2001.

BI: *Dust sample element analysis in PPM for Stichting VISIE Amsterdam*, Hangar-8, Schiphol Oost. Tagarp (Sweden): Biospectrum International AB, July 1998. (www.web-light.nl).

BNL: News release. New York: Brookhaven National Laboratory, July 18, 2000. (www.bnl.gov).

Bramhall, R.: *Risks from depleted uranium*. The Lancet, vol.357, May 12, 2001, p.1532.

Busby, C.C.: *Wings of death; Nuclear pollution and human health*. Aberystwyth: Green Audit Books, 1995. (www.llrc.org/2ndevent/2ndeventpage.htm).

Busby, C.C.: *Recalculating the 'Second Event' error; A reworking of the probabilities of Second Event damage to cells relative to natural background radiation*. Münster: Low Level Radiation Symposium, March 1998. (www.llrc.org/2ndevent/subtopic/secevnew.htm).

Busby, C.C.: *Reply to the Commentary on the Second Event Theory of Busby by A.A. Edwards and R. Cox*. International Journal of Radiation Biology, vol.76, no.1, 2000, pp.119-125. (www.llrc.org).

Busby, C.C.: *Depleted uranium in Kosovo*; Review of the UNEP report of 13th March, 2001. Aberystwyth: Conference, April 4, 2001. (www.llrc.org/du).

Cajar Páez, A: *Rastro del uranio empobrecito*. La Prensa (Panama), 19 January 2001.

Castanier, C. et Chareyron, B.: *Uranium appauvri; La banalisation d'un déchet radioactif toxique*, in Barrillot et al, 2001, pp.29-50.

Castañón Blanco, F.: *Spanish KFOR troops and Balkans syndrome report*. June 10, 2001.

Catalinotto, J. and Flounders, S.: *Is the Israeli military using depleted uranium weapons against the Palestinians?* New York: Depleted Uranium Education Project (International Action Centre), November 27, 2000. (www.iacenter.org/israel_du.htm).

CH: *Projecto radiativitade da Fondação Bradesco. Ciência Hoje*, vol. 28, November 2000.

Chepetsky: *Depleted uranium, reliable biological irradiation shielding*. Chepetsky Mechanical Plant, 2001. (www.udm.ru/chepetskyzavod.html).

Collon, M.: *The 'NATO syndrome'; Arms, profits and lies; Who has been concealing the dangers of depleted uranium for the last ten years and why?* New York: International Action Center, January 18, 2001. (www.iacenter.org/depleted).

Comité: *Petición del Comité pro rescate y desarrollo de Vieques ante el Comité de descolonización de las Naciones Unidas. Vieques*, Puerto Rico: CPRDV, 2001. (www.cprdv-peticion.htm).

Cowan, D.N., DeFraites, R.F., Gray, G.C., Goldenbaum, M.B. and Wishik, S.M.: *The risk of birth defects among children of Persian Gulf War veterans*. The New England Journal of Medicine, vol.336, June 5, 1997, pp.1650-1656.

Dai, S., Burleigh, M.C., Haire, M.J., Myers, E., Zhang, Z., Konduru, M.V. and Overbuy, S.H.: *Putting depleted uranium to use; A new class of uranium-based catalysts*. Tucson: Acts of the Waste Management Conference, March 2001.

De Brouwer, Ch.: *Y a-t-il un développement durable pour les populations exposées aux poussières d'uranium appauvri?* Une approche du risque de santé, in Barrillot et al. 2001.

DHC: *Review on uranium and depleted uranium*. Amsterdam: Dutch Health Council, May 2001. (www.web-light.nl).

de Jonge, H.: *Depleted uranium measured in Amsterdam 6 years after El Al crash; uranium 236 is also measured*. June 5, 2000, in VISIE, 2001.

DoD: *Environmental exposure report; Depleted uranium in the Gulf (II)*. Washington: Department of Defense, December 13, 2000. (www.gulflink.osd.mil/du_ii).

DoD: *Department of Defense studies medical impact of depleted uranium in the Balkans*. Washington: Department of Defense, October 30, 2001. (www.usembassy.it).

DoD-IP: *Information paper on depleted uranium environmental and medical surveillance in the Balkans*. Washington: Department of Defense, October 25, 2001. (www.deploymentlink.osd.mil/du_balkans).

DoD-NT: News transcript. Washington: Department of Defense, January 4, 2001. (www.defenselink.mil/news/jan2001).

DoE: *Uranium recycle material processing*. Oak Ridge Operations, US Department of Energy, report no. ORO-859, September 1985. (A copy may be requested from Tara Thornton, Military Toxics Project, duorganizer@igc.org).

Dole, L.R., Mattus, C. and Spence, R.: *Heavy concrete for spent fuel and waste storage silos*. Tucson: Acts of the Waste Management Conference, March 2001.

Doyle, P., Roman, E. and Macnochie, N.: *Risk of birth defects among children of Persian Gulf War veterans*. The New England Journal of Medicine, vol.337, October 16, 1997, pp.1175-1176.

DUMP: *Depleted uranium and uranium alloy properties*. Depleted Uranium Management Program (USA), 1999. (web.ead.anl.gov/uranium).

Durakovic, A.: *Medical effects of internal contamination with uranium*. Croatian Medical Journal, vol.40, nr.1, 1999, pp.49-66. (www.vms.hr).

Durakovic, A.: *On depleted uranium: Gulf War and Balkan syndrome*. Croatian Medical Journal, vol.42, nr.2, 2001, pp.130-134. (www.vms.hr).

Durakovic, A., Dietz, L. and Horan, P.: *Quantitative analysis of uranium isotopes in Canadian, US, and British Gulf War veterans*. Uranium Medical Research Centre, October 4, 2001.

EAD: *Programs/projects*. Environmental Assessment Division, US Department of Energy, 2001. (www.ead.anl.gov/project).

EC: *Opinion of the group of experts established according to article 31 of the Euratom treaty ; Depleted Uranium*. Brussels; European Commission, 6 March 2001.

Edwards, A.A. and Cox, R.: *Commentary on the Second Event Theory of Busby*. International Journal of Radiation Biology, vol.76, no.1, pp.119-125, 2000. (www.llrc.org/2ndevent/subtopic/ijrb.htm).

Edwards, A.A. and Cox, R.: *Response to a letter of C. Busby*. International Journal of Radiation Biology, vol.76, no.1, 2000, p. 125.

Elder, J.-C. and Tinkle, M.C.: *Oxidation of depleted uranium penetrators and aerosol dispersal at high temperature*. Los Alamos National Laboratories, report LA-86110-MS, December 1980.

EPI: *Summary report to Congress on health and environnmental consequences of depleted uranium use by the US Army*. US Army Environmental Policy Institute, June 1994. (www.fas.org)

EXP: *Depleted uranium in the Gulf*. Washington: Department of Defense, Environmental Exposure Report, December 13, 2000. (www.gulflink.osd.mil/du_ii).

Euler, C.A.: Médecins du Monde, *Report on an International scientific conference on environmental consequences of the Balkan crisis*. Athens, January 26, 2001. (www.publica.cz).

Euler, C. and Parker, K.: *Depleted uranium munitions; The use of radiological weapons as a violation of human rights.* United Nations Sub-commission on the promotion and protection of human rights, 51st session, August 1999. (www.webcom.com/hrin/parker).

Fahey, D.: *Depleted uranium weapons; Lessons from the 1991 Gulf War.* Amsterdam: Laka Foundation, May 1999. (www.antenna.nl/wise/uranium/#DU).

FAS: *Tip of the iceberg? Apparent use of depleted uranium in bombs and missile systems.* Washington: Federation of American Scientists, February 25, 2001. (fas.org/man/dod-101/usaf/docs/mast).

Federal Register: *Decommissioning of DU munitions test area at Jefferson Proving Ground (Indiana, USA).* December 16, 1999.

Feynman, R.: *Cargo cult science,* in Surely you're joking, Mr. Feynman! New York: Norton, 1985.

Fisk, R.: *The evidence is there; We caused cancer in the Gulf.* The Independent, October 16, 1998.

Forsberg, C.W.: *Repository applications for depleted uranium (Fill, Cermet, and Invert).* Tucson: Acts of the Waste Management Conference, March 2001.

FR: Notice; *Decommissioning of DU munitions test area at Jefferson Proving Ground (Indiana).* The Federal Register (USA), December 16, 1999.

Fulco, C.E., Liverman, C.T., Soc, H.C. (eds.): *Gulf war and health, vol.1: Depleted uranium, pyridostigmine bromide, sarin, and vaccines.* Washington: National Academy Press, 2000.

Goldblat, J.: *Arms control; A guide to negotiations and agreements.* Oslo: Peace Research Institute (PRIO), 1996.

Goodhead, D.: *Oral presentation on the Second Event Theory of Busby.* Symposium on the health effects of low level radiation, London, April 24, 1996.

Grover, D., Krahn, S., Martin, Ch., Miller, C., Tontodonato, R. and Yeniscavich, W.: *Integrity of uranium hexafluoride cylinders.* Defense Nuclear Facilities Safety Board, technical report, May 5, 1995. (web.ead.anl.gov/uranium/documents).

GSF: GSF News, 5 February 2001. (www.gsf.de)

Haire, M.J. and Price, R.R.: *Technical review of depleted uranium uses research and development program.* Washington: Office of environmental management, Department of Energy, January 16, 2001. (www.ornl.gov/~webworks/cppr/y2001/pres)

Hansard (record of the UK Parliament): Session of 7 February 2001, information given by the Ministry of Defence.

Harley, N.H., Foulkes, E.C., Hilborne, L.H., Hudson, A. and Ross Anthony, C. (1999): *A Review of the scientific literature as pertains to Gulf War illnesses, vol.7: Depleted uranium.* RAND (National Defense Research Institute) Corporation, 1999. (www.rand.org/publications).

HLP: *Human rights and toxics; Depleted uranium and the Gulf War.* Humanitarian Law Project, International Education Development ; United Nations Commission on human rights, 53rd session, March 1997. (www.webcom.com/hrin/parker).

HLP: *Violations of human rights.* Humanitarian Law Project, International Education Development; United Nations Commission on human rights, 57th session, March 2001.

Hooper, F.G.: *Elevated urine uranium excretion by soldiers with retained uranium shrapnel.* Health Physics, vol.77, 1999, pp.512-519.

Hooper, M.: Response to the Royal Society report on '*The health hazards of depleted uranium munitions, part I*', Manchester: CADU, June 14, 2001. (http://www.cadu.org.uk/info/reports/hooper.htm)

HRAC: *Depleted uranium.* Washington: Health Risk Assessment Consultation, Department of Defense, September 15, 2000. (www.gulflink.osd.mil).

HRIN: Archives of briefs, statements and country reports. Human Right Interactive Network, The Karen Parker home page for humanitarian law; Autumn 2001. (www.webcom.com/hrin/parker.html)

Hug, P.: Private communication, 11 December 2000.

Hutchings, G.J. and Heneghan, C.S.: *Uranium-oxide-based catalysts for the destruction of volatile chloro-organic compounds.* Nature, vol.384, 1996, pp.341-343.

IALANA: *News.* International Association of Lawyers Against Nuclear Arms, The Hague (www.ialana.org/site/main.html).

ICTY: *Final report to the Prosecutor by the Committee established to review the NATO bombing campaign against the Federal Republic of Yugoslavia.* International Criminal Tribunal for the former Republic of Yugoslavia, June 2, 2000. (www.un.org/icty/pressreal/nato061300.htm).

IDUST: *Report on Cruise missiles.* International Depleted Uranium Study Team, January 27, 2001.

Ismal, K., Everitt, B., Hull, N., Unwin, C., David, A. and Wessely, S.: *Is there a Gulf War syndrome ?* The Lancet, vol.353, 1999, pp.179-182.

ITA: *US domestic exports,* 1999 and 2000 year-to-date. OTEA, 2001. (www.ita.doc.gov/td/industry/otea/trade-detail).

Iyer, R. and Lehnert, B.E.: *Radiation-induced effects in unirradiated cells.* Science and Medicine, January/February 2000, pp.54-63.

Jaeggi, P. (ed.): *Quand mon enfant est né, j'ai ressenti une grande tristesse.* Basle: Lenos, 2000.

Jane's: '*Dense metal' penetrators.* Jane's Defence website, July 11, 1997. (www.janes.com/defence).

Jane's: *Depleted Uranium.* Jane's Defence Weekly, January 8, 2001.

Jane's-LF: *Pakistan joins DU producer nations.* Jane's Land Forces website, May 9, 2001.

Jourdan, A.: Annecy a joué avec le feu en ignorant une pollution à l'uranium. *La Tribune de Genève*, 15 September 2001.

Kang, H., Magee, C., Mahan, C., Lee, K., Murphy, F., Jackson, L. and Matanoski, G.: *Pregnancy outcome among U.S. Gulf War veterans; A population-based survey of 30 000 veterans.* Annals of Epidemiology, vol.11, October 2001, pp.504-511.

van der Keur, H.: *Uranium pollution from the Amsterdam 1992 plane crash; Risk of depleted uranium exposure admitted by the parliamentary inquiry commission probe.* Amsterdam: Laka Foundation, May 1999, in WISE, 2001. (www.antenna.nl/wise/uranium/dhap997.html).

van der Keur, H: *Where and how much depleted uranium has been fired ?* Communication at the Campaign Against Depleted Uranium (CADU) conference on depleted uranium. Manchester, November 4, 2000.

Kirby, A.: Uranium weapon fears in Kosovo (BBC News, April 9, 1999); *Pentagon confirms depleted uranium use* (BBC News, May 7, 1999); *Pentagon's man in uranium warning* (BBC News, May 11, 1999); *Depleted uranium; The lingering poison* (BBC News, June 6, 1999); *Depleted uranium; A soldier's experience* (BBC News, June 7, 1999).

Kovaleski, S.F.: *A dangerous American legacy; Acres of U.S. military land in Panama are littered with unexploded munitions.* The Washington Post, April 2, 1998.

Laka: *Pakistan producing depleted uranium munitions.* Amsterdam: Stichting Laka, March 14, 2001.

Lenhert, B.E.: *Radiation bystander effects.* Dateline Los Alamos, July 2001.

Lindsay-Poland, J.: *Pentagon study of ranges in Panama reveals explosive problems.* San Francisco: Fellowship of Reconciliation Bulletin, no.19, Spring 1997.

Lopez, D.: *Conference on health and environment consequences of depleted uranium used by US and British forces in the 1991 Gulf War, Baghdad,* December 2-3, 1998.

Lopez, D.: *Radiation readings near Basrah.* International Depleted Uranium Study Team (IDUST), 23 January 2001.

MacFarlane, C.J., Thomas, E. and Cedry, N.: *Mortality among UK Gulf War veterans.* The Lancet, July 1, 2000, pp.17-21.

Mara, L., Thieme, B. e Caldiroli, M.: *Indagine in Kosovo sull'inquinamento da uranio impoverito.* Milano: Medicina Demcratica e Centro Regionale di Intervento per la Cooperazione, September 1999.

Mara, L., Thieme, B. e Caldirola, M.: *Rischi, malattie e morte da uranio impoverito.* Milano: Medicina Democratica, 2001.

Marusic, A. and Ramsay, S.: *NATO doctors question 'Balkan war syndrome'.* The Lancet, vol.357, January 20, 2001, p.201.

McBride, J.: *Cornered Dutch minister blames Israel over El Al crash.* Reuters, July 21, 1999.

McNeil, R.: *Lockerbie fears over missing Uranium.* The Observer, June 1, 1990; also in VISIE, 2001.

FMedact: *Why depleted uranium should not be used in War* (a Medact briefing), 2001. (www.medact.org).

Meek, T. and Haire, M.J.: *Uranium based semicondoctors.* Washington: Office of environmental management, Department of Energy, January 16, 2001. (www.ornl.gov/~webworks/cppr/y2001/pres).

Mesler, B.: *The Pentagon's radioactive bullet.* The Nation, October 21, 1996.

Mitchell, J.: *When US hand over bases to Panama, it may leave environmental mess behind.* The Christian Science Monitor, August 20, 1997. (www.csmonitor.com/durable/1997/08/20/intl/intl.3.html).

MoD: *Testing for the presence of depleted uranium in UK veterans of the Gulf conflict; The current position.* London: Ministry of Defence, March 24, 1999.

MoD: *Research into Gulf War veterans' illnesses.* London: Ministry of Defence, 2000.

MoD-MP: *Report on the visit to Kosovo by members of the MoD Enhanced Environment Monitoring Program Team,* January 19-23 2001. London: Ministry of Defence, January 2001.

Mould, R.F.: *Depleted uranium and radiation-induced lung cancer and leukaemia.* The British Journal of Radiology, vol.74, 2001, pp.677-683.

MSC: *Industrial depleted uranium metal areas of civilian applications.* Tennessee: Manufacturing Sciences Corporation, 2001. (www.mfgsci.com/metprod.html).

Nagasawa, H. and Little, J.B.: *Unexpected sensitivity to the induction of mutations by very low doses of alpha-particle radiation; Evidence for a bystander effect.* Radiation Research, vol.152, November 1999, pp.552-557.

NASY: *The poisoning of Yugoslavia; Interview with Dusan Vasiljevic.* North American Solidarity with Yugoslavia, August 7, 1999. (http://come.to/the.green.table).

NATO: *Depleted uranium; A short course.* Brussels: NATO, December 13, 2000.

NATO: *UNEP confirms U [236] found in DU penetrators.* Brussels: NATO, January 16, 2001. (www.nato.int/docu/speech/sp2001.htm).

NATO-B: *Briefing.* Brussels: NATO, January 10, 2001. (www.nato.int/docu/speech/2001).

NATO-BI: *Background information.* Brussels: NATO, February 2, 2001. (www.nato.int/du).

NATO-D: *Declaration of the secretary general on the use of depleted uranium ammunitions in the Balkans.* Brussels: NATO, January 10, 2001. (www.nato.int/docu/speech/2001).

NATO-I: *Information. Data concerning the locations of depleted uranium ordnance expended during Allied Operations Deny Flight- Deliberate Force, 1993-95 in Bosnia.* Brussels: NATO, January 14, 2001. (www.nato.int/du/docu).

NATO-Ia: *Information. Data concerning the locations of depleted uranium ordnance expended during Allied Operation Force.* Brussels: NATO, January 24, 2001. (www.nato.int/kosovo/docu).

NATO-S: *Statement.* Brussels: NATO, January 18, 2001. (www.nato.int/kosovo/docu).

Nazario-Delgado, C.M.: *La salud en Vieques. Puerto Rico: Escuela graduada de salud pública,* September 2001, and private communication, 21 November 2001.

Nau, I.-Y.: *La France va lancer une enquête épidémiologique.* Le Monde, 25 April 2001.

NRPB: *Fire at a Royal ordnance factory.* Nuclear Radiation Protection Board, Response statement no. R2/99, February 8, 1999.

NRPB: *Questions about depleted uranium.* National Radiation Protection Board, September 18, 2001.

NuDat: *Nuclear data retrieval, uranium.* New York: National Nuclear Data Center, 2000.

Parker, R.L.: *Fear of flying.* Nature, vol.336, December 1988, p. 719.

Parker, K.: Statement. International conference: Campaign Against Depleted Uranium (CADU), Manchester, 4 November 2000. (www.webcom.com/hrin/parker).

Pike, J.: *Guided Bomb Unit-28 (GPU-28) penetrator.* The Federation of American Scientists, February 22, 1998. (www.fas.org).

Price, R.R., Haire, M.J. and Croff, A.G.: *Depleted uranium uses R & D program.* Tucson: Acts of the Waste Management Conference, March 2001.

Priest, N.: *Toxicity of depleted uranium.* The Lancet, vol.357, January 27, 2001, pp.244-245.

PSOB: *Hearings of the Presidential Special Oversight Board.* Washington: George Washington University, July 13, 1999.

Raabe, O.G.: *A short review of depleted uranium toxicity.* Jane's, January 12, 2001. (www.janes.com).

RAMA: *Depleted uranium munitions, Nellis Range renewal.* Lassen County: Rural Alliance for Military Accountability, 1999.

Ramachandra, K.B.: *Review of transuranics in depleted uranium armor.* Department of the Army (USA), January 19, 2000.

RAND: *A review of the scientific literature as pertains to Gulf War illnesses* (12 vol. publiés jusqu'à maintenant). RAND (National Defense Research Institute) Corporation, 1999. (www.rand.org/publications).

Red Betances: *Perfil de la salud en Vieques,* Puerto Rico. Red Betances, Información sobre Puerto Rico y sus luchas, 2 October 2001.

Repacholi, M.H.: *Background material on depleted uranium (DU).* NATO, January 8, 2001. (www.nato.int/kosovo/docu).

Ristic, D., Benderic, R., Vejnovic, Z., Orlic, M. and Pavlovic, S.: *Ammunition produced from depleted uranium.* Belgrade: Institute of Nuclear Sciences 'Vinca', 1997. (www.prop1.org/2000/du).

Roberts, A. and Guelff, R.: *Documents of the laws of war* (3rd edition). Oxford: Oxford University Press, 2000.

Roth, P., Werner, E. and Paretzke, H.G.: *A study of uranium excreted in urine; An assessment of protective measures taken by the German Army KFOR Contingent* (Research report prepared for the Federal Ministy of Defense). Neuherberg: Institute of Radiation Protection, January 2001. (www.nato.int/du/docu/ge010229a.pdf).

Roussel, P.: *L'uranium et les armes à l'uranium appauvri (avec quelques compléments et une mise à jour).* Orsay: Institut de physique nucléaire, November 2001.

Royal Society: *The health hazards of depleted uranium munitions; Part I.* London: The Royal Society, May 22, 2001. (http://www.royalsoc.ac.uk/policy/cur_du.htm).

Ruiz-Marrero, C.: *Vieques residents alarmed by depleted uranium reports.* Inter Press Service, January 30, 2001.

Schmid, E. and Wirz, Ch.: *Depleted Uranium.* Spiez: Laboratorium Spiez, May 2000. (www.vbs.admin.ch/acls).

Sharma. H.: Private communications, 2001.

SIPRI: *Selection of DU weaponry in the registers of the transfers and licensed production of major conventional weapons, 1988 to 1999,* in World armaments and disarmament, Stockholm International Peace Research Institute, yearbooks 1988 to 1999. New York: Oxford University Press.

Sito-Susic, D.: *Bosnians blame depleted uranium for rise in cancer.* Kasindo, February 5, 2001.

SO: *Indian police seize depleted uranium from scrap dealer.* The Sunday Observer (India), May 6, 2000. (www.prop1.org/2000/du).

Der Spiegel, 10-2-'01.

UEN: *Newsletter*, December 2000/January 2001. (www.earthisland.org).

Uijt de Haag, P.A.M., Smetsers, R.C.G.M., Witlox, H.W.M., Krüs, H.W. and Eisenga, A.H.M.: *Evaluating the risk for depleted uranium after the Boeing 747/258F crash in Amsterdam,* 1992. Journal of Hazardous Material, vol. A 76, 2000, pp. 39-58.

UMRC: *Independent study to determine abundance of depleted uranium, DU, in the urine of exposed veterans and civilians.* Uranium Medical Research Centre (Canada), 2001. (www.umrc.net).

UNEP: *The potential effects on human health and the environment arising from possible use of depleted uranium during the 1999 Kosovo conflict; A preliminary assessment.* Geneva: United Nations Environment Program, October 1999. (http://www.grid.unep.ch/btf/missions/september/dufinal.pdf).

UNEP: *News release; NATO confirms to the United Nations use of depleted uranium during the Kosovo conflict.* Geneva: United Nations Environmental Program,

21 March, 2000. (www.grid.unep.ch/btf/pressreleases/unep21032000.html).

UNEP: *Depleted uranium in Kosovo; Post-conflict environmental assessment.* Geneva: United Nations Environmental Program, 2001. (http://postconflict.unep.ch/publications/uranium.pdf)

UP: *Depleted Uraniun fact file.* Uranium Program, U.S. Department of Energy, Office of Environmental Management, 2001.

US Navy: *Survey work plan for depleted uranium penetrators,* Vieques Naval Target Range, Live Impact Area, Vieques, Puerto Rico. March 21, 2000.

USSCVA: *Report of the special investigation unit on Gulf War illnesses.* Washington: United States Senate Committee on Veterans' Affairs, 1998.

VA: *Information from the Department of Veterans Affairs,* 21 March, 2000. (www.va.gov/nchp/gulf).

VISIE: *Burning depleted uranium; a medical disaster.* Amsterdam: Stichtig VISIE, 2001. (www.web-light.nl).

Vujanovic, D.: *The cemetery in Bratunac already stretches to the houses.* 12 January, 2001. (www.nedeljnitelegraf.co.yu).

WebElements: Uranium. 2001. (www.webelements.com).

Wilcox, J.: *Vieques, Puerto Rico; An island under siege.* American Journal of Public Health, vol.91, May 2001, pp.695-698.

Williams, G.P., Hermes, A.M., Policastro, A.J., Hartmann, H.M. and Tomasko, P.: *Impact from range fires at Aberdeen Proving Ground,* Maryland. Argonne National Laboratories, March 1998. (www.ead.anl.gov/pub).

WISE: Uranium Project. Amsterdam: World Information Service on Energy, 2001. (www.antenna.nl/wise/uranium).

WISE-URP: *Uranium radiation properties,* 1 September, 2000, in WISE, 2001. (www.antenna.nl/wise/uranium/rup.html).

WHO: *Depleted uranium; Sources, exposure and health effects.* Geneva: World Health Organisation, April 2001.

Yacoup, A., Al-Sadoun, I. and Hassan, G.G.: *Further evidence on relation between depleted uranium and incidence of malignancies among children in Basra, Southern Iraq.* International Conference on depleted uranium, health, ecological and economical problems, Gijón (Spain), November 2000.

Zajic, V.S.: *Review of radioactivity, military use, and health effects of depleted uranium.* August 1999. (members.tripod.com/vzajic).

Zuza, Z.: *Balkan syndrome; Acquittal without investigation.* Banja Luka, 27 March, 2001.

Part III
Afterword

Depleted Uranium Weapons:
The Whys and Wherefores

by André Gsponer

Abstract

It is recalled that the only non-nuclear military application in which depleted uranium alloys outperform present day tungsten alloys is long rod penetration into a main battle tank's armour. However, this advantage is only of the order of 10%, and it disappears when the uranium versus tungsten comparison is made in terms of actual lethality of complete anti-tank systems instead of laboratory type homogeneous armour steel penetration capability. Therefore, new micro and nano engineered tungsten alloys may soon be at least as good, if not better, than uranium alloys, enabling the production of tungsten munitions which will be better than existing uranium munitions, and whose overall life cycle cost will be lower, due to the absence of the problems related to the radioactivity of uranium.

The reasons why depleted uranium weapons have been introduced into arsenals and used in Iraq and Yugoslavia are analysed from the perspective that their radioactivity must have played an important role in the decision making process. It is found that depleted uranium weapons belong to the diffuse category of low radiological impact nuclear weapons to which emerging types of low yield (i.e., fourth generation) nuclear explosives also belong.

It is concluded that the battlefield use of depleted uranium in the 1991 Gulf War, which broke a 46 year long taboo against the intentional use or induction of radioactivity in combat, has created a military and legal precedent which has trivialized the combat use of radioactive materials, and therefore made the use of nuclear weapons more probable.

1 Introduction

When conventional weapons containing depleted uranium were used for the first time in combat during the 1991 Gulf War, there was an immediate reaction from the general public, environmental groups and anti-nuclear activists. This reaction has now turned into a major environmental, medical, technical, legal and political opposition with

126

many thousands of 'anti-depleted uranium activists' in many countries striving to outlaw the use of depleted uranium in weapons and consumer goods.

What drove this reaction was common sense. Indeed, while there had been little public or parliamentary opposition to the development and deployment of conventional weapons containing depleted uranium before the Gulf War, the immediate consequence of their *actual use* in Iraq was the realization that uranium (whether natural, enriched, or depleted) is not a trivial material that can be placed in the same category as tungsten or steel. In fact, it was this same commonsense understanding of the deep political significance of the military use of a radioactive material that drove the only parliamentary reaction, by Senator Bob Dole, to the 1978 decision by the US Department of Defense to use depleted uranium for making bullets[1].

Of course, an important reason for the lack of significant early opposition to the military use of depleted uranium is that its radiological impact is very much lower than that of existing types of nuclear weapons: atomic and hydrogen bombs.

As is well known, depleted uranium is only about half as radioactive as natural uranium, which is a low radioactive material. But being radioactive means that any uranium based material is *qualitatively* different from any non-radioactive material, and therefore means that any use of uranium has important medical, technical, legal, and political implications. Moreover, there is no doubt that these differences have always been perfectly understood in professional circles, as is witnessed by the considerable amount of legislation dealing with all types of radioactive materials, and the special efforts that had to be made, for example in the United States, to release depleted uranium for commercial use[2], and to enable it to be incorporated in 'conventional' weapons and possibly exported to foreign countries[3].

The only context in which the use of depleted uranium could have been 'benign' is that of a nuclear war. This is why many people perceived armour piercing munitions containing depleted uranium as a tolerable part of a strategy to deter a massive tank attack by the nuclear armed Warsaw Pact Organization. But Iraq in 1991 did not have nuclear weapons. This made the first use of depleted uranium weapons during the 1991 Gulf War, which broke a 46 year long taboo against the intentional use or induction of radioactivity in combat, particularly shocking.

It is therefore understandable that there have been a lot of over-reactions. On the one side many opponents predicted apocalyptic consequences on the environment and the affected populations, and on the other side many governmental and official bodies counter-reacted by excessively downplaying the consequences of the use of depleted uranium weapons.

There have been many articles, both in newspapers and in professional journals, discussing the near and long term environmental, medical, and radiological consequences of depleted uranium weapons. On the other hand, there have been surprisingly few published investigations on the whys and wherefores of depleted uranium weapons – namely the technical and military reasons why they were first introduced into arsenals, and the strategic political reasons why they were then used against Iraq and former Yugoslavia, two non-nuclear weapon states.

In particular, it appears that there is no published critical study of the much vaunted superiority of uranium-based over tungsten-based anti-tank weapons, despite the fact that several major countries, most prominently Germany, have equipped their tank fleets with tungsten-based anti-tank weapons which are claimed to be good enough to defeat the armour of all existing tanks. In fact, as will be seen in section 2, this paradox is easily dismissed by looking at the professional literature, which shows that while penetrators made of tungsten alloys are somewhat inferior to depleted uranium ones, the overall performance of tungsten-based anti-tank weapons is no worse than that of their uranium based counterparts.

Moreover, it appears that there is no published critical study that focuses on the only fundamental property that distinguishes uranium from its competitors, namely the fact that it is radioactive, and examines it from the point of view of its strategic and political consequences.[4] In effect, the numerous studies in which radioactivity is taken into account are only those dealing with the environmental, medical, and legal consequences of the combat use of depleted uranium.

The only exception seems to be a study in which the radiological effect due to the large scale battlefield use of depleted uranium is compared to that of existing and hypothetical fourth generation nuclear weapons[5]. This study will be reviewed in section 3.3 and put into perspective with other elements which suggest the conclusion that possibly the most powerful institutional force behind the development and deployment of depleted uranium weapons must have been the 'nuclear lobby,' which in all nuclear weapon states is pushing towards the trivialization of the use of nuclear materials of all kinds, and of nuclear weapons of current or future types.

In this section, therefore, an attempt will be made to understand the 'whys and wherefores' of depleted uranium weapons – the technical and military advantages which could have justified their introduction into arsenals, and the political and strategic reasons which could explain their actual battlefield use, despite the environmental, medical, legal, and political drawbacks which were known long before they were developed and used. In section 3 this attempt will be merged with what is already better known about depleted uranium weapons, and a conclusion derived to give additional arguments for an immediate ban on depleted uranium weapons of all kinds.

2 Are uranium alloys really better than
tungsten alloys for conventional weapons?

In a number of civilian and military applications the decisive physical characteristic of a material is its density. The next decisive parameter is usually cost, which means that the material should be made of an element that is reasonably abundant on Earth. If the density has to be as high as possible, the choice must be between four elements, namely tungsten, uranium, tantalum, and hafnium, which have as maximum density 19.2, 19.0, 16.7, and 13.3 respectively. By comparison, in crystal rocks, these elements are all about ten times less abundant than lead, density 11.3, which itself is about a thousand times less abundant than iron, density 7.8.

The main technical reason why high density materials are important in conventional weapons comes from the so-called 'Root Density Law,' a very simple result that can be derived as an exercise by students of a final year high school physics class. It says that when a rod of length L, made of some material of density p_1, penetrates at very high velocity another material of density p_2, the maximum penetration length under ideal conditions is $\sqrt{p_1/p_2} \times L$. By 'ideal conditions' it is meant that the two materials interact so fast and violently at their contact interface that they immediately melt, which is why these conditions are named the 'hydrodynamic limit.' However, even below this limit, the Root Density Law is pertinent for comparing processes where kinetic energy is exchanged between materials of different densities.

For example, in the case of a tungsten or uranium anti-tank penetrator of length L, the absolute maximum penetration depth into homogeneous steel is $\sqrt{19/7.8} \times L = 1.5 \times L$. This means that the penetration power into homogeneous steel armour is at most 50%

129

higher for a tungsten or uranium rod than for a steel rod. Therefore, in all applications where the Root Density Law applies, and where steel is replaced by a higher density material, the potential benefit is at most 50%.

Moreover, if instead of comparing the differences between the use of a high density versus a low density material, one compares the differences between the use of one high density material with that of another high density material (i.e., a uranium alloy versus a tungsten alloy), the differences to be expected from the unavoidable disparities in the respective mechanical properties of the two alloys will necessarily be smaller than 50% in any application where the conditions of use are close to the 'hydrodynamic limit.' In other words, when one is discussing the merits and demerits of using a uranium instead of a tungsten alloy, one is in fact discussing small differences of the order of 10–20%, not large differences which could turn a uranium based weapon into a 'super weapon' compared to the same weapon made out of tungsten. Therefore, the whole discussion in this section turns on the impact of relatively small mechanical and metallurgical differences between various alloys based on either uranium or tungsten. Indeed, if these two elements had the same physical and chemical properties, and would therefore form similar alloys when combined with other elements, the obvious choice would be tungsten – and in most cases uranium would immediately be discarded because of its radioactivity.

The problem is that in the conditions where the disparities in mechanical properties of different alloys have a visible impact, i.e. below the hydrodynamic limit, there are many concurrent processes in which each of these disparities has a different effect. If one property is favourable in some process, it will not necessarily be so in another one. Therefore, there is no alloy, based on either uranium or tungsten, which has at the same time all the desirable properties. The result is that the choice of a given alloy is a compromise, and this is reflected in the fifty year long history during which either tungsten or uranium alloys have been considered as the 'best' for one weapon's use or another[6].

To understand where we stand today, we have to review the major conventional weapons applications in which high density materials are used:
● Penetration aids for bombs or cruise missiles;
● Shield plates for armoured tanks;
● Munitions for anti-tank weapons;
● Munitions for ground attack aircraft or close-in-defence guns.

130

These four sets of applications are discussed in the next subsections, which are organized in a logical sequence – the information given in each one is useful to understand the next.

2.1 Penetration aids for bombs or cruise missiles

In these applications, the high density material is used to give more weight and a slender profile to the weapon, for example a freefall or rocket-assisted bomb, so that it will have more kinetic energy per unit frontal area when hitting the target (an airport runway, a bunker, etc.). This enables the warhead to penetrate deeper into the target before the explosive is detonated by a delayed fuse, which enormously increases the damage. Obviously, in such applications it is mandatory that the nose of the penetrator, as well as the casing enclosing the warhead, remain functional as long as possible. Their strength and hardness therefore need to be as high as possible. From all that is known about the respective mechanical properties of uranium and tungsten alloys, the first choice is then clearly tungsten[7]. Where the warhead is a nuclear bomb, one option could be to prefer a natural uranium alloy because its nuclear properties could make it part of the last stage of a thermonuclear explosive. However, this may put excessive constraints on the design of the nuclear payload, and it is likely that a separate forward-posted tungsten penetrator will be preferred.

In the case of long-range cruise missiles, the same reasoning applies, with the difference that weight considerations have a different impact on the design. This is because a cruise missile is both a delivery system and a bomb. If too much weight is given to the warhead, the range of the cruise missile will be considerably shortened. Moreover, there is an obvious trade-off between the amount of high explosives that is carried and the weight of the penetration aid. Either the conventional warhead is made as powerful as possible (or eventually replaced by a nuclear explosive) and the weapon is detonated on the surface or at a shallow depth into the target, or else some quantity of high explosive is sacrificed to increase the weight of the penetrator in order to gain a factor which may be as large as ten in the case of a deep penetration. The trouble is that the impact velocity of a cruise missile is not as large as that of a bomb. The impact conditions are even likely to be well below the 'hydrodynamic limit,' so that little benefit is to be expected from the Root Density Law. A strong steel penetrator could therefore be just as good as a heavy metal penetrator, and the possibility that the cruise missiles

131

used in the Gulf War or in Yugoslavia carried a heavy metal penetrator is only a speculation since 'there is no publicly available information at all that supports such an assumption' (Lilios: 1999:165)[8].

2.2 Shield plates for armoured tanks

In the case of this application, it is important to know that the shield of a modern battle tank is designed to protect the crew and the main components (engine, gun, ammunition, fuel tank) from a large range of threats: conventional and nuclear bombs, shaped charges delivered by bazookas or precision guided munitions, anti-tank rounds fired by enemy tanks or heavy guns, landmines, etc. For these reasons the shield of such a tank is a complicated structure comprising several layers of materials of different densities, interspaced with composite or fibrous materials, and possibly covered with reactive components such as high explosive charges which automatically detonate to interfere with or destroy the darts or penetrators of anti-tank weapons.

If one focuses on anti-tank rounds fired by enemy tanks or heavy guns, also called 'kinetic energy projectiles,' the decisive element of a tank shield is that the main structural material, a thick layer of armour steel, is supplemented by one or two other layers, or arrays of plates, made of some tough material able to deflect, bend, break, or at least slow down the anti-tank projectiles so as to prevent them from fully penetrating the main armour. The effectiveness of this shielding mechanism has been demonstrated in many tanks built in the past decades. From recent publications it appears, for example, that a long rod penetrator emerging through a 1 cm thick steel plate hit at high obliquity has a residual penetration capability of only about 50% of that of the original rod[9]. This shows that the 'obliquity advantage' of designing armoured vehicles with glacis and sloped walls is quite important, and explains why anti-tank weapons capable of penetrating more than 60 cm of homogeneous armour steel are needed in order to defeat the armour of modern tanks (Lanz:2001).

Therefore, an array of relatively thin steel plates, positioned obliquely in front of the main armour, has a considerable shielding effect. This effect can be further enhanced by the use of 'sandwiches' in which steel plates are combined with layers of plastic or ceramic materials, or by replacing the steel with some higher density material. This calls for a hard high-strength heavy alloy, with tungsten the first choice again, even though the US incorporated steel clad depleted uranium plates in the M1 tanks deployed in Iraq during the Gulf War. However, contrary to the first two applications in which the 'Root Density Law' could bring an improvement of up to 50%, the incorporation of heavy alloys in armour has only a marginal effect on the overall performance of the shield, especially if the heavy material plates are made thinner than the original steel plates to keep the total weight constant.

Moreover, the difference between using uranium instead of tungsten will have an even more marginal effect, because there is no mechanical property of importance in this application that is very significantly different between alloys of either of these two materials.

2.3 Penetrators for anti-tank weapons

In this application, the discussion is more complicated because a number of distinct physical phenomena, which imply conflicting requirements on correlated mechanical properties, have to be taken into account. For instance, anti-tank penetrators are first accelerated in a gun, where they are submitted to very high stress, vibrations, etc., until they exit from the gun muzzle where they violently separate from the 'sabot' that was holding them during acceleration; secondly, they travel through air, where they can break because of bending or buckling; and thirdly, they eventually encounter a tank shield, where everything is designed to defeat their action.

These three are, in gunnery jargon, the internal, external, and terminal ballistics problems – to which one has to add the lethality problem, because piercing an armour is not enough to inflict damage or loss of function behind the armour. Therefore, whereas in the applications considered in the two previous subsections the problem naturally led to a single set of requirements to be met by the properties of the material, and thus to relatively unsophisticated uranium or tungsten alloys, in the tank armour penetration application no single alloy has simultaneously the ideal properties suiting the requirements of the three ballistic problems. For this reason, over the past fifty years small differences between successive generations of uranium and tungsten alloys have resulted in either the former or the latter being perceived as 'better or worse' for one ballistic phase or another, or for the anti-tank ballistic problem as a whole.

To discuss these problems it is best to start from the target and work backwards to the gun, and then add overall performance and lethality considerations at the end. Moreover, in the perspective of assessing the possible advantages of the use of uranium instead of tungsten, we will concentrate on the long rod penetrators that are fired by the 120mm guns which today equip most of the main battle tanks in service in the major Western powers' armies. Typically, these penetrators are heavy material rods of about 60 cm in length and 2 cm in diameter. Therefore, according to the Root Density Law, the maximum penetration depth should be about 60×1.5 = 90 cm in homogeneous armour steel, while the observed maximum is only about 60 cm for penetrators shot by a tank gun. This is because the impact velocities of tank fired projectiles are in the range of 1200 to 1700 m/s, which corresponds to a transition region somewhat below the hydrodynamic limit that is reached only in laboratory experiments where velocities of about 4000 m/s are achieved[10].

The slow evolution in heavy metal alloy physics and metallurgy which led to such a penetration capability is described in a number of papers, for example Rostker (2000) and Davitt (1980), which emphasize depleted uranium alloys and the 1950 – 1980 period, and Lanz et al. (2001) which emphasizes tungsten alloys and the more recent period. In this evolution, the yardstick for comparing various alloys has become the depth of penetration in 'Rolled Homogeneous Armour' (RHA) steel, i.e., the best possible armour steel.

This gives a very telling and impressive figure of merit, which is however only *one* parameter of importance in the anti-tank ballistic problem. Nevertheless, without entering into the historical details, whereas tungsten alloys were in general favoured from the late 1950s until the early 1970s, the preference started to shift in the United States towards uranium alloys in the mid-1970s after the successful development of a new uranium alloy containing 0.75% per weight titanium[11]. This alloy overcame several technical and manufacturing problems that previously gave the preference to tungsten. Moreover, the penetration capability of this $U{:}\frac{3}{4}Ti$ alloy in RHA steel was consistently better than any tungsten alloy of equal density. This improvement was the more impressive in that the $U{:}\frac{3}{4}Ti$ holes into RHA steel were both deeper and narrower than those produced by tungsten alloys, all other things being equal.

At the beginning, of course, the exact numbers showing how much the new uranium alloy was better than the tungsten alloys available at the time were classified[12]. But since at least 1990 they are given in numerous unclassified professional publications[13]. There are also numerous publications in which the overall average advantage of uranium alloys over tungsten alloys is given as a single number. For

134

example, S.P. Andrews et al., working on contract for the US Army, claim that 'the ballistic performance of DU alloys and tungsten alloys against monolithic semi infinite steel targets is similar – at best 5 to 10% difference'[14]. Similarly, R.J. Dowding of the U.S. Army Research Laboratory at the Aberdeen Proving Ground, states that 'depleted uranium alloys outperform tungsten alloys by 10% at ordnance velocities'[15].

Looking at the data, one finds, as expected, that the penetration advantage of uranium over tungsten alloys is less pronounced for high velocity projectiles because the conditions are closer to the hydrodynamic limit. For instance, comparing the penetration efficiencies at 1200 and 1700m/s impact velocities, the advantages are 25 and respectively 5% in Magness and Farrand (1990:Fig.3), 20 and 15% in Pengelley (1994:43), and finally 25 and 15% in Farrand et al. (2001:Fig.2). But these numbers should be taken with caution. While they clearly demonstrate an advantage of about 10 to 20% over the velocity range of interest for anti-tank weapons, they derive from 10 drawings that are quite poor according to normal scientific standards: there are no error bars and the figures are clearly drawn to impress the non-specialists (especially in Pengelley). Therefore, since these data constitute the main (if not *only*) objective element that supports the thesis that uranium alloys are more effective than tungsten alloys for anti-tank weapons, it is important to stress that this relatively small effect is the basis of much of the depleted uranium controversy, because most of the depleted uranium expended in Iraq was precisely in the form of anti-tank penetrators.

A second interesting feature shown by the data is that the penetration dynamics of uranium rods are different from that of tungsten rods with the same dimensions and weight. Normally, when a rod of some material penetrates at high velocity into a target material, a mushroomed region forms near the impacting end, and its nose erodes (as the penetrator burrows into the target) by giving up material that is 'back extruded' from the penetrator target interface while the interface moves forward into the target. This process is explained and illustrated in many papers[16], as well as in computer animations available on the internet[17]. The interesting feature, which was first observed with the U:$\frac{3}{4}$Ti uranium alloy penetration data, is that while all available tungsten alloys retained a mushroomed head during the full penetration process, the U:$\frac{3}{4}$Ti uranium alloy penetrators formed a chiseled nose which resulted in the boring of a narrower channel which led to deeper penetration than tungsten

(Magness and Farrand:1990). Unfortunately this factual observation led to many simplified and exaggerated statements, which can even be found in the professional literature, that somehow tungsten penetrators have necessarily a 'large mushroomed head,' while only uranium penetrators would have a 'self sharpening nose.'

In reality, the 10 to 20% penetration advantage discovered around 1975 with uranium alloys is due to a small effect that was apparently not properly understood until 1990, when Magness and Farrand published the correct explanation. According to them, the reason why U3/ 4Ti uranium alloy penetrators keep a narrow profile during penetration is a metallurgical effect called 'adiabatic shear banding', which implies that failures develop in the highly stressed nose region in such a way that the edges of the mushroomed head are quickly discarded, producing a sharpened or chiseled nose[18]. This shearing effect is small, as can be seen in shallow penetration simulations, such as Stevens (1996), yet it is sufficient to produce the 10 to 20% effect in deep penetrations which, according to numerous accounts, is claimed to be the main reason for deciding to produce large numbers of uranium penetrators since the late 1970s.

Soon after the origin of this technical advantage of uranium alloys was understood, and therefore shown not to be due to any fundamental difference between uranium and other heavy materials, a considerable impetus was given to many research programmes that were trying to find better alloys of tungsten and other materials (i.e., tantalum and hafnium) to replace and possibly outperform uranium alloys. The realization that 'adiabatic shear behaviour ... aids the performance by minimizing the size of a mushroomed head on the eroding penetrator' (Magness and Farrand:1990:473), along with 'concerns over environmental problems' (Andrew et al.:1992:249) and depleted uranium's 'drawbacks: health and safety, cost of cleanup, environmental impact, political' (Dowding:2000:4), all led to worldwide efforts to find substitute materials for uranium based anti-tank weapons alternatives that would be 'without the perceived hazards and political difficulties associated with DU' (Magness et al.:2001:1188). To this effort anti-nuclear activists have substantially contributed by raising the public and parliamentary awareness of the problems associated with depleted uranium.

. For example, soon after the Gulf War, an ambitious programme was initiated in South Korea, where the proximity of China (the world's largest producer of tungsten), the proximity of large potential markets such as Japan, and the uncertainties of its relations with

North Korea, led to more than 13 patents and 23 scientific papers in less than ten years[19]. In this, and other research programmes[20], the emphasis is on finding a tungsten or tantalum alloy, or an amorphous material based for example on hafnium, or even a more complex nano-crystalline material produced by nano-technology (Magness et al.:2001), that would exhibit adiabatic shear behaviour and have the other required properties to be used for anti-tank penetrators. Apparently, these programmes are getting close to achieving their objectives and it remains to be seen whether these technical advances will translate into environmentally more acceptable anti-tank weapons.

However, while these technical developments are clearly important to improve one aspect of the terminal ballistic problem, one should not forget that they will potentially yield only a small contribution to the overall performance of an anti-tank system. Moreover, there is an even more important consideration: does the perceived advantage of adiabatic shearing, namely a deeper but narrower penetration tunnel, really translate into a higher tank lethality? The answer is almost certainly no! The reason is that the motivation for seeking deeper but narrower penetration tunnels is the use of a single figure of merit, *the penetration depth into semi infinite RHA steel (penetration criterion)*, which does not take into consideration that the purpose of piercing armour is to inflict damage behind the armour: the penetration depth merely says that armour of such a thickness will just be perforated, with little energy left to inflict damage or loss of function behind the armour. Therefore, a more realistic figure of merit is to take, for example, *the complete perforation of a finite thickness of RHA steel plate' (perforation criterion)*. In effect, in that case some energy is left after perforation to inflict some damage behind the armour (Farrand et al.:2001). Using this simple change in the figure of merit, it was found that whereas using the traditional *penetration criterion* uranium penetrators outperform tungsten penetrators by about 15 to 25%, (ibid:Fig.2), using the *perforation criterion* there is no longer any significant difference between uranium and tungsten penetrators, (ibid:Fig.3). The explanation of this important result is easily found, and related to the fact that tungsten penetrator tunnels are wider than uranium penetrator tunnels: 'uranium penetrates RHA much more effectively than tungsten; however, tungsten will produce a larger breakout effect. Therefore, the two processes may cancel each other out, depending on the predominant failure mechanism of the target evaluated' (ibid:1163). This result, obtained after a detailed discussion of the complicated problem of objectively defining the protection level (or seen from the other perspective, the kill probability) of an armoured vehicle, shows that serious methodological issues are still to be resolved by the designers of armoured vehicles and anti-armour weapons.

Indeed, even though the United States and a few other countries have proclaimed in the past 25 years that uranium-based anti-tank weapons were far better than others, several major countries, most prominently Germany[21], have not equipped their tank fleets with these, but instead have continuously improved the mechanical properties and the metallurgy of the tungsten alloy used in their anti-tank penetrators (Lanz et al.:2001). And it turns out from what is known that these weapons are good enough to defeat the armour of any existing tank. How is that possible? A realistic criterion for objectively assessing the capabilities of these weapons is obviously the first step. But there are other, more direct technical reasons. For instance, some crucial mechanical properties which are important during the acceleration of the penetrator in a gun are significantly worse for uranium than for tungsten penetrators. 'DU penetrators therefore need stiffer and heavier sabots than tungsten rods, which compensates for the slightly better impact behaviour of DU in RHA' (ibid:1194). In simpler language: what is gained by uranium alloys in the armour penetration phase, is lost in the initial launch phase and during the flight to the target. But this does not close the discussion: many more effects should be considered, especially in the interaction with complex multi-layer tank shields and even more so in the assessment of the lethality behind the armour. However, as we have repeatedly stated, each of these effects has little impact on the overall performance, so that whatever difference could exist between the properties of one or another heavy alloy of tungsten or uranium, they are much more likely to cancel each other out than to cumulate and give a small advantage to either of them.

This is also true for one property that we have not yet considered, *pyrophorism*: finely pulverized uranium spontaneously ignites in air. This dramatic effect certainly adds a lethality component to uranium which tungsten, for example, does not have. However, when a tank penetrator emerges behind an armour, it generates an intense shower of melted metallic fragments and particles which can badly burn the personnel, ignite the fuel tank, or detonate the munition in the ammunition store. This is true whatever material the penetrator is made of, and it it likely that these breakout effects are more important for tungsten than for uranium penetrators. Moreover, a modern main battle tank may be equipped with a controlled atmosphere to protect against chemical weapons and avoid the propagation of fires: there could be little oxygen for uranium to burn. Nevertheless, the pyrophoric nature of uranium adds a degree of lethality, which may increase the level of overkill of a weakly shielded armoured vehicle defeated at short range, but not to such a degree that it could significantly increase the kill radius of anti-tank rounds intended to defeat the best shielded main battle tanks.

2.4 Munitions for ground attack aircraft or close-in defence guns

In this last set of applications, the previous considerations about tank shields and kinetic energy anti-tank weapons mean that the discussion can be quite short. Ground attack aircraft, such as the A10 of the United States Air Force, have been designed and deployed 'to counter massive Soviet/Warsaw Pact armoured formations spearheading an attack into NATO's Central Region (by firing armour-piercing incendiary rounds) designed to blast through top armour of even the heaviest enemy tanks' (Rostker:2000). There are thus two elements to assess: the armour piercing and the incendiary capabilities of the munition. First, as is now amply demonstrated, the penetration superiority of uranium penetrators corresponds to only a (small) effect in the case of long rod penetrators plunging into thick armour: this is not the case for ground attack projectiles which are much less slender than long rod penetrators, and which are intended to defeat the relatively thin top armour of battle tanks and the walls of relatively lightly armoured vehicles such as personnel carriers. Tungsten projectiles would be just as good. As for the incendiary effect of A10 projectiles due to the pyrophoric properties of uranium, it has not been possible to find any professional level paper in which it is compared to the incendiary effect of tungsten shells containing an incendiary substance. Nevertheless, since the pyrophoric property of uranium is not such that most of it will burn on impact, it can be inferred that a tungsten shell containing a sufficient amount of a truly effective incendiary substance could be just as devastating.[22]

Finally, it remains to discuss the use of heavy materials in munitions for close-in weapon systems, such as the US Navy 'Phalanx' designed to provide a last ditch defence against sea-skimming missiles. In this application the main reason for using heavy metals is that a smaller and slimmer bullet has a significantly better external ballistics trajectory, which increases the precision of the system.

On the other hand, since sea-skimming missiles (or for that matter most types of precision guided munitions and cruise missiles) are relatively 'soft' targets, the armour penetration capabilities of heavy metal alloys are of secondary importance. The interesting aspect in the history of this application is that after deciding in 1978 to use a uranium alloy, the US Navy decided in 1989 to change to tungsten alloys, 'based on live fire tests showing that tungsten met their performance requirements while offering reduced probabilities of radiation exposure and environmental impact' (Rostker:2000). After this change from uranium to tungsten, further developments were made on the projectile, and a new tungsten alloy led to 'improved ballistic performance by 50% compared to existing tungsten alloy penetrators'[23]. While nothing is said about the reasons for this improvement, it most probably comes from the superior internal ballistics behaviour of tungsten projectiles, which allows a tungsten bullet to be launched at a higher velocity than a uranium bullet.

3 Are depleted uranium weapons conventional or nuclear weapons?

A central element in the depleted uranium controversy is that on the one hand it is both radioactive and usable in civilian and military applications of nuclear energy, and that on the other hand the proponents of its 'non-nuclear' uses claim that it can be treated as interchangeable with a heavy material such as tungsten. This leads to questions ranging from 'Is depleted uranium a nuclear or conventional material?' to 'Are depleted uranium weapons conventional or nuclear weapons?' as well as to more fundamental questions such as 'What is a nuclear material?' or 'What is a nuclear weapon?' (And the converse where the adjective nuclear is replaced by conventional because 'conventional' may not necessarily mean the same as 'non-nuclear'.)

These are perfectly reasonable questions, but they are very difficult to answer without taking many technical, legal, political, and even historical considerations into account. A comprehensive analysis is not possible in a single paper, and certainly not in a paper written by a single author. Nevertheless, it is possible to give a reasonable first answer to the question 'What is a nuclear material or weapon?' and thus to develop useful pointers to answering the other questions. Moreover, in relation to depleted uranium weapons, it is possible to present some important elements, which have not been much discussed in the published literature, showing that their combat use cannot be separated from the potential use of nuclear weapons. This is what will be done in the next three subsections.

3.1 Nuclear and conventional materials

Article XX of the Statute of the International Atomic Energy Agency (IAEA), which came into force in July 1957, defines a *nuclear material* as being either a *source material* or a *special fissionable material*. In simplified language, which hides many technical and legal subtleties, a *special fissionable material* (e.g., uranium enriched in the isotopes 235 or 233, plutonium, etc.) is any fissionable material that has been artificially transformed or produced to make it more suitable for use in a nuclear reactor or a fission explosive; and a *source material* (e.g., natural uranium, uranium depleted in the isotope 235, thorium, etc.) is any material suitable for transformation into a special nuclear material (by enrichment, transmutation, etc.). Therefore, the term *nuclear material* covers all materials which may be used, either directly or after transformation, in a nuclear reactor or in the core of a *fission* explosive, i.e., an 'atomic bomb,' in which a self sustaining chain reaction takes place. Consequently, the term *non-nuclear material* covers all other materials, even though they include light elements such as tritium and lithium which are the main source of the explosive power of a *fusion* explosive, i.e., a 'hydrogen bomb.' On the other hand, article XX makes no *qualitative* distinction between natural uranium and depleted uranium, which are therefore both nuclear materials.

In practice, such definitions, which have the merit of being clear and consistent with both physical facts and common sense, were bound to create difficulties because of the dual use characteristics, i.e., military and civilian, of nuclear materials. Therefore, as soon as the IAEA tried to implement its role in the safeguard of nuclear materials, it had to introduce a quantitative element in order to establish a complicated accounting system for tracing the flow of nuclear materials throughout the world: 'effective weights' were assigned to nuclear materials on a subjective scale where, for example, 1 tonne of depleted uranium would be equivalent to only 50 grams of special fissionable material[24] even though 1 tonne of depleted uranium could contain several kilograms of uranium 235. At the other end of the spectrum, to deal with problems related to plutonium and highly enriched uranium, further definitions had to be introduced, e.g., the term *nuclear weapon usable material* to designate nuclear materials that can be used for the manufacture of nuclear explosive components without transmutation or further enrichment.

The result was the beginning of a process which facilitated the non-military uses and the international trade of nuclear materials, while at the same time stretching out the scale used to classify these materials. Consequently, the materials sitting at either end of the scale started to become exceptions of one type or another. At one end, nuclear weapon usable materials became more and more inaccessible to the non-nuclear weapon states, with nuclear weapon states exerting more and more direct pressure on those states, e.g., Yugoslavia, who had some amount of nuclear weapon usable materials on their territory[25]. At the other end, the same nuclear weapon states made a lot of effort to trivialize the use of the main by-product of the nuclear industry: depleted uranium.

This can clearly be seen in United States legislation[26], but also in international agreements such as the London Guidelines, which make exceptions for 'source material which the Government is satisfied is to be used only in non-nuclear activities, such as the production of alloys or ceramics'[27]. In this guideline, 'Government' refers to the exporting country, which means that such a government is authorized to allow the export of depleted uranium for the purpose of making, for example, tank penetrators.

This 'stretching out' process, which reflects the growing tension between nuclear weapon states and non-nuclear weapon states, or would-be nuclear weapon states, is also visible in the evolution of concepts such as 'peaceful nuclear activities' and 'proliferation prone nuclear activities.' While nuclear weapon states insist on the peaceful and benign character of their broad and extensive nuclear activities, they impose very narrow and restrictive definitions of these activities by others. This was particularly visible in 1991 when the IAEA was requested by the Security Council to carry out immediate on-site inspection in Iraq: for the first time, all activities prone to nuclear weapons proliferation had to be explicitly and comprehensively defined in an annex to a Security Council resolution so that the inspection team had a clear mandate to work from (Gsponer et al.:1997:appendix). This annex confirmed IAEA's definitions of nuclear materials, but introduced other definitions and restrictions, such as the prohibition of the production of 'isotopes of plutonium, hydrogen, lithium, boron and uranium,' which placed in the same category materials that are of importance to both nuclear and thermonuclear weapons (ibid:11).

To conclude this subsection, it can be asserted that the concept of nuclear material as defined by the Statute of the IAEA is still valid today. Therefore, depleted uranium is definitely a nuclear material according to international law, even though there is a trend to trivialize its use in so-called 'non-nuclear applications.'

This trivialization clearly contradicts the legal status of the material, as well as the jurisprudence, because it is impossible to prove that a nuclear material is used 'only in non-nuclear activities'[28] or 'solely to take advantage of (its) high density or pyrophoric characteristics'[29]. In fact, such 'declarations of intent' are used as the main element in the laborious arguments put forward by those who argue that depleted uranium weapons are neither radiological nor nuclear weapons[30]. Similar kinds of 'declarations of intent' are used instead of factual evidence to assert that depleted uranium weapons are neither incendiary nor chemical weapons, despite the pyrophoric and toxic properties of uranium.

3.2 Nuclear and conventional weapons

The words of most international arms control agreements, such as the *Nuclear Non-Proliferation Treaty (NPT)* and the *Comprehensive Test Ban Treaty (CTBT)*, do not include definitions of essential terms, such as 'nuclear weapon' or 'nuclear explosion,' even though these terms refer to what is controlled or prohibited by the treaties. The reason is the difficulty of defining them in unambiguous technical language that would be acceptable to all parties. The definition and interpretation of these terms are therefore left to each individual party, which may share its interpretations confidentially with other parties, or possibly make them public in a declaration.

Consequently, in order to learn about what is really understood by the terms 'nuclear weapon' and 'nuclear explosion' one must analyse the declarations made by many countries, the statements they made during the negotiations, the opinion of leading technical and legal experts, etc. Such an analysis is outlined in Gsponer and Hurni (2000) where it is shown that the current practical definition of a 'nuclear explosion' is much narrower that one would intuitively think. In fact, what is strictly forbidden by the CTBT are not explosions in which any kind of nuclear reaction would produce some militarily useful explosive yield, but only explosions in which a diverging fission chain reaction takes place. This is very far from the idea of a treaty stipulating 'not to carry out any nuclear test explosion or any other nuclear explosion' (Article I of the CTBT) and leaves open the possibility of designing and testing new types of nuclear weapons in which no diverging fission chain reaction takes place.

In fact, this research is happening throughout the world, not just in the laboratories of the nuclear weapons states, but also in the major industrial powers such as Japan and Germany. Using gigantic laser facilities, such as the US National Ignition Facility (NIF), France's Laser Mégajoule, Japan's GEKKO at Osaka, and similar tools in Germany and other countries, enormous progress is being made towards the design of small fusion bombs in full compliance with the CTBT – which does not fully restrict the explosive use of nuclear fusion, unlike nuclear fission. This activity is now the main advanced weapons research priority of the nuclear weapons laboratories, which claim that its purpose is just the 'stewardship' of stockpiled nuclear weapons. It is also the main route towards the controlled release of fusion energy in countries such as Japan and Germany, which claim that these small fusion explosives are only for peaceful applications.

As for defining the term 'nuclear weapon,' the main source of difficulty is that the least unambiguous characteristics of the intuitive concept of a nuclear weapon are of a qualitative and subjective rather than quantitative and objective nature. Indeed, it is the enormity of the difference in the destructive power of nuclear weapons compared to conventional weapons that has historically led to the qualitative distinction between 'nuclear' and 'conventional' weapons. Similarly, it was their indiscriminate nature, and their targeting of cities rather than military forces, which led to the concept of 'weapons of mass destruction.' Consequently, it is now difficult to argue that weapons made of a nuclear material like depleted uranium are nuclear weapons, or even that new types of weapons in which a nuclear explosion takes place that is not forbidden by the CTBT are nuclear weapons.

It appears, therefore, that the most commonly accepted definition of a 'nuclear weapon' – that is of an enormously destructive weapon – has created a situation in which less potent weapons based on similar materials or physical principles, and producing similar effects, but on a smaller scale, have become acceptable to governments as if they were 'conventional weapons.'

For example, when the British Under Secretary of State for Defence, states that: 'Nuclear, biological and chemical weapons are indiscriminate weapons of mass destruction specifically designed to incapacitate or kill large numbers of people. DU ammunition is not'[31].

He is right. However, he is ignoring an important element that lies at the root of the 'dialogue of the deaf' that characterizes the depleted uranium debate, namely that depleted uranium *is* a nuclear material, that it *is* radioactive, and that this *has* important consequences – especially in relation to nuclear weapons. It can therefore be argued that depleted uranium weapons are *not* conventional weapons.

Similarly, the fact that the explosive yields of the laboratory scale fusion explosions that will be produced in a few years, for example at the US National Ignition Facility, will correspond to only a few kilogram equivalent of TNT does not mean that these explosions are not nuclear explosions, which in fact they *are* according to both physics and common sense.

3.3 Depleted uranium and fourth generation nuclear weapons

As we have just seen, the huge difference in the damage produced by a single 'city busting' nuclear weapon compared to the impact of conventional weapons has led to the contemporary situation in which a radioactive material such as depleted uranium is routinely used on the battlefield, and in which new types of nuclear explosives are being designed. These nuclear explosives could have yields in the range of 1 to 100 tonne equivalence of TNT, i.e., in the gap which today separates conventional weapons from nuclear weapons which have yields equivalent to thousands or millions of tonnes of TNT.

These new types of nuclear explosives are called fourth generation nuclear weapons[32]. This name refers to a terminology in which the first generation corresponds to 'atomic' or 'nuclear' bombs, and the second to 'hydrogen' or 'thermonuclear' bombs. The third generation corresponds then to the 'tailored' or 'enhanced' effects warheads such as the Enhanced Radiation Warhead (ERW, also called a neutron bomb) which were never deployed in large numbers because they never found any truly convincing military use. Moreover, since these third generation weapons still had the high yields and large radioactive fallouts characteristic of the first two generations they could not be used on the battlefield as if they were some kind of trivial tactical weapon.

In comparison to the previous generations, fourth generation nuclear explosives are characterized by the following features :
- They will not contain a significant amount of nuclear weapon usable material (i.e., plutonium or highly enriched uranium) in which a self-sustaining diverging chain reaction could take place, so that their development and testing will not be forbidden by the Comprehensive Test Ban Treaty;
- They will produce relatively little radioactive fallout and residual radioactivity, because they will contain little or no fissile material at all;

• They will derive the bulk of their explosive yield from fusion (which is why they may be qualified as 'pure fusion' explosives) rather than from fission or other nuclear reactions, so that their radioactive effects will be those induced by fusion;

• They will have relatively low explosive yields, so that they will not qualify as weapons of *mass* destruction.

Consequently, compared to the third generation, fourth generation nuclear explosives are much more likely to find numerous military applications. In particular, it is well known that the amount of conventional explosive that is delivered by precision guided munitions like cruise missiles (i.e., 50 to 100 kg of chemical high explosives) is ridiculous in comparison to their cost: some targets can only be destroyed by the expenditure of numerous delivery systems while a single one loaded with a more powerful warhead could be sufficient. Therefore, the availability of fourth generation nuclear warheads with yields in the range of 1 to 100 tonne equivalence of TNT will constitute a very dramatic change in warfare, a change that can only be compared to the first use of nuclear weapons in 1945 or the first deployment of intercontinental ballistic missiles in 1959. Indeed, fourth generation nuclear weapons will have yields a thousand times larger than conventional weapons, that is a thousand times smaller than nuclear weapons of the previous generations, which means that they are much more likely to be used on the battlefield than first, second, or third generation nuclear weapons, especially since they correspond to a strongly perceived military need.

In practice, while proponents of fourth generation nuclear weapons may convincingly argue that just like depleted uranium weapons they are not weapons of mass destruction, that they can be used in discriminate ways, etc., it will be more difficult for them to dismiss the fact that they nevertheless produce effects that do not exist with conventional explosives: namely an intense burst of radiation during the explosion, and some residual radioactivity afterwards.

The proponents will therefore argue that the burst of radiation (mostly high energy fusion neutrons) will affect only the target area, and that the only long term collateral damage will be the 'low' residual radioactivity due to the dispersal of the unburnt fusion fuel and to a smaller extent to the interaction of the neutrons with the ground, the air, and the materials close to the point of explosion.

It is at this stage of the critical assessment of the military consequences of the potential use of fourth generation nuclear weapons that an important finding was made: *The expenditure of many tonnes of depleted uranium has a radiological impact comparable to that of the combat use of many kilotons TNT equivalent of pure fusion nuclear explosives.*

This finding, which is reported by Gsponer and Vitale in the Proceedings of the Fourth International Conference of the Yugoslav Nuclear Society, Belgrade, Sept.30-Oct. 4, 2002, was very surprising at first. This is because it was totally unexpected that the radiological impact of the battlefield use of depleted uranium could be compared to that of the battlefield use of a large number of hypothetical fourth generation nuclear warheads. But this is what the laws of physics, and what is known about the effects of nuclear radiation on human beings, imply: the use of depleted uranium weapons creates a residual radioactive environment that provides a yardstick which can be used by the proponents of fourth generation nuclear weapons to demonstrate that the radioactive burden due to their use is 'acceptable.'

For instance, it is found by Gsponer and Vitale that the expenditure of one tonne of depleted uranium in the form of bullets has a long-term radiological impact equivalent to the use of many kilotons of hypothetical pure fusion weapons. This means that between 100 and 1000 precision-guided munitions (which today deliver only 10 to 100 kilograms of high explosives), each carrying a pure fusion warhead with a yield of 1 to 10 tonnes of high explosive equivalent, could be used to produce a similar radiological impact. Since about 400 tonnes of depleted uranium were used in Iraq, and about 40 in Yugoslavia, the radiological impact in these countries corresponds to that of using tens of thousands of precision-guided munitions tipped with fourth generation nuclear weapons, i.e., many more precision-guided delivery systems than were actually used in these countries.

Thus, while depleted uranium weapons create a low radioactive environment, this radioactive burden is not less negligible than the predictable radiological impact of the new types of nuclear weapons that are under development. The battlefield use of depleted uranium has therefore created a military and legal precedent for the use of nuclear weapons which produce a radioactive burden that is much less than that of existing types of nuclear weapons, but which have a destructive power about a thousand times larger than conventional explosives.

4 Discussion and conclusion

In this paper two important new contributions have been made to the depleted uranium debate: (1) a critical appraisal of the conventional weapon's use of heavy materials showing that depleted uranium alloys have no truly significant technical or military advantage over tungsten alloys for that purpose; and (2) an analysis showing that depleted uranium weapons cannot be classed as conventional weapons and that they belong to the diffuse category of low radiological impact nuclear weapons to which emerging types of nuclear explosives also belong.

These contributions serve to complete and reinforce the numerous arguments that have been put forward to show that depleted uranium weapons are illegal according to international law and contrary to the rules of war. They also clarify the discussion of the reasons why depleted uranium weapons have been made and why they were used in Iraq and Yugoslavia.

Since the main battlefield use of depleted uranium was in anti-tank weapons, let us review and critique six of the more obvious military reasons that must have played a role in the decision to use them against Iraqi and Serbian armour:

1. *The most effective ammunition available had to be used in order to get quick results.* Depleted uranium munitions are at best only marginally more effective than tungsten munitions. Moreover, the majority of Iraqi tanks were not of the latest Soviet generation (such as the T80), and the use of depleted uranium rounds in Yugoslavia against lightly armoured tanks and personnel carriers was a gross overkill. In fact, just as effective (and less costly) non-radioactive anti-tank weapons were available in large numbers during both the Iraqi and Yugoslavia campaigns.

2. *Depleted uranium munitions have the additional advantage that uranium is pyrophoric.* The incendiary effect of depleted uranium anti-tank rounds is only a marginal contribution to their tank lethality effect. On the other hand, the pyrophoric property of uranium is the *main* short-term cause of the dispersion of uranium in the environment.

3. *Depleted uranium munitions were available but had never been tested on the battlefield.* Their use in 1991 broke a 46 year long taboo against the intentional battlefield use of radioactive materials. It is therefore particularly shocking that during the Gulf War the British Ministry of Defence quickly adapted depleted uranium ammunition developed for the new Challenger 2 tank so as to use it on the existing Challenger 1 tank fleet. This meant that the munition could be labelled 'combat proven' after the war.

4. *Depleted uranium is a radioactive material which inspires pride in its users, fear in its victims, and strong reactions in the bystanders.* Indeed, depleted uranium long rod penetrators are the 'favourite rounds' of tank gunners and the 'least acceptable rounds' to a large share of public

opinion and environmental activists. Consequently, the numerous and often excessive reactions of the anti-depleted uranium activists unwittingly contributed to the military propaganda machine by amplifying the military psychological advantage of using depleted uranium instead of a non-radioactive material.

5. *Depleted uranium weapons have an overall long-term radiological effect comparable to that of pure fusion nuclear weapons.* As for the previous reason, there is no direct evidence that this reason was taken into account at some stage of the decision making process. However, the analysis by Gsponer and Vitale (2002), as well as considerable indirect evidence[33], show that the military planners[34] are acutely aware of the *full* consequences of using depleted uranium and the lessons that can be learned from its use. In particular, it is indisputable that the use of a radioactive material in Iraq and Yugoslavia has created a military and legal precedent. Similarly, it is indisputable that this use has provided a first test of the acceptability of future weapons that would produce a low level of radioactivity. In fact, the use of depleted uranium weapons has proved to be acceptable, both from a military point of view because the induced radioactivity did not impair further military action, and from a political standpoint because most political leaders, and shapers of public opinion did not object to their battlefield use.

6. *Depleted uranium weapons are less expensive than tungsten weapons.* This reason has been left for the end because it is not strictly speaking a military reason and because it is fallacious in two respects. First, it is clear that the cost of a single anti-tank round that is capable of destroying, or saving, a main battle tank is marginal in comparison to the cost of such a tank. Therefore, using a phrase that is much used in such a context, if 'gold plating' would improve the performance of anti-tank rounds, they would all be gold plated!

Consequently, it can be asserted that even if depleted uranium were more expensive than tungsten and depleted uranium rounds were only marginally better than tungsten rounds, uranium rounds would still be preferred by the military. Second, it turns out that the market value of depleted uranium is artificially low because it is a surplus of the nuclear industry. However, this low price of the raw material proves to be misleading: the additional costs incurred by choosing uranium (processing difficulties, problems due to pyrophorism and radioactivity, clean-up of the environment after use, etc.) mean that the full *lifecycle cost* of uranium is much higher than that of tungsten.

Therefore, if the full lifecycle cost is taken into account, the preference easily goes to tungsten, an observation that the tungsten industry has not failed to make[35]. To sum up, in a situation such as the 1991 Gulf War where a full range of anti-tank weapons was available – including a number of tungsten anti-tank weapons, which it would have been opportune to compare in combat to uranium ones – the price argument was truly of secondary importance.

Reflecting on these military reasons, one sees that they basically take the same line of argument that is always developed in order to justify the introduction of some new controversial weapon. In the case at hand, there are even strong echoes of the 'neutron bomb debate' of the mid 1980s[36]. In that debate, the proponents presented the neutron bomb as an almost magical super weapon that would defeat a Soviet tank invasion without producing large collateral damage to the surrounding towns and cities. The argument was shown to be plain wrong by simply making an analysis of modern tank armour technology and by calculating the protection that would be provided by such armour against the neutrons from a neutron bomb[37]. Similar analyses were made in section 2 (where a rather long argument was required to complete the proof that depleted uranium rounds are not 'silver bullets') and Gsponer and Vitale (2002), using only published professional papers, and purely scientific arguments. The conclusions are that depleted uranium weapons are not super weapons of any kind, and that their perceived military advantages, as well as their perceived environmental disadvantages, are vastly exaggerated by both the proponents and the opponents of these weapons.

In the case of the neutron bomb debate, it turned out that rational and measured arguments had a remarkable impact on the outcome of the debate, which turned to the advantage of the opponents. It is therefore of interest to see what such arguments can say about the possible reasons *why* depleted uranium weapons have been put into arsenals despite the numerous environmental, medical, technical, legal, and political objections that have been anticipated, and are still raised against their fabrication, deployment, and use.

First of all, as can be seen in the professional literature, of which the bibliography of this paper only gives a limited overview, there has been a lively debate between ballistic weaponeers about the merits and demerits of depleted uranium versus tungsten projectiles. This debate has been running for fifty years now, and the use of depleted uranium in Iraq and Yugoslavia has only reinforced the convictions of the weaponeers opposed to depleted uranium. In fact, while the US

Navy had already reverted to tungsten years before the Gulf War, and the US Air Force has now decided that its next generation tank killer will not use depleted uranium, no country that had decided against depleted uranium penetrators changed its policy after 1991[38].

Second, there are the well known facts that the price of depleted uranium has been made artificially low in order to encourage its use, and that the price of tungsten (like that of other strategic materials) is mainly a function of political decisions such as the level of releases from the huge stockpiles maintained in Russia and the United States. Moreover, there is the observation that the unclassified American technical literature is clearly biased in that it mostly refers to the performance of anti-tank *penetrators* rather than to the performance of complete anti-tank weapon *systems*[39]. All of this suggests that the push towards the use of depleted uranium has been much stronger than was ever justified by a small perceived advantage of uranium alloys over tungsten alloys in one specific application: long rod penetration into homogeneous armour.

Third, there is a long history of events showing that the 'nuclear lobby' (which in the 1950s and 1960s was the incarnation of 'progress and modernity') has always had a very strong influence on the course of economic and military affairs in all the nuclear powers. In particular, one can see its influence in the politics behind the development of new nuclear weapons, for example the neutron bomb, or new sources of nuclear energy, for example micro-explosion fusion. It is tempting to speculate that a policy which consists of making the price of a material like depleted uranium as low as possible is both an investment for the future and a way to trivialize the use of radioactive materials in all circumstances.

Finally, there is the very grave military and legal precedent created by the combat use of a radioactive material, which is a clear violation of the spirit, if not the letter, of a norm that was in force since 1945. To argue that nobody holding a position of competence or responsibility was aware of the full consequences of breaking this norm would be quite unreasonable. On the contrary, considering the existence of a lively internal debate on the consequences of the battlefield use of depleted uranium and other nuclear materials, it is certain that these had been thoroughly investigated long before 1991. One must admit, therefore, that the choice made in favour of using depleted uranium took into account the fact that its battlefield use would trivialize the military use of radioactive materials, and would therefore make the use of nuclear weapons more probable.

In conclusion, it can be argued that besides its military function, the use of depleted uranium in Iraq and Yugoslavia must have served a political purpose: to prepare for the progressive introduction of fourth generation nuclear weapons whose battlefield use will cause a low (but non-negligible) residual radioactive environment. It may even be possible to argue that depleted uranium was used in Iraq – and then in Yugoslavia where there were few military reasons for using it – in order to test the opposition of the Western public opinion to the introduction of radioactivity on the battlefield, and to get the world population accustomed to the combat use of depleted uranium and fourth generation nuclear weapons.

Endnotes

1. Making Bullets Out Of Depleted Uranium – Mr. Dole: 'Mr. President, an article appeared in the Washington Star on March 14, reporting that the Pentagon is about to start using depleted uranium to produce bullets. They seem to have chosen this material for bullets because uranium metal is dense, and because depleted uranium is cheap. Needless to say, I find this proposal shocking. On the one hand this shows a complete lack of sensitivity to the general fear of using radioactive materials. On the other hand, only a strange set of policy decisions could have made this material so cheap that anybody would consider using it for bullets.' Opening paragraph of statement by Senator Bob Dole at the 95th Congress, 2nd session, Vol. 124 (part 29) March 17, 1978, page 7416.

2. Back in 1971 the Atomic Energy Commission initiated a rule permitting the commercial use of depleted uranium. See proposed amendment at Federal Register 40, No. 7, January 10, 1975, pp. 2209–2211.

3. The US International Security and Development Cooperative Act of 1980 states that 'depleted uranium may be sold upon a finding that an export of uranium depleted in the isotope U-235 is incorporated in defense articles or commodities solely to take advantage of the high density or pyrophoric characteristics unrelated to its radioactivity. Such exports shall be exempt from the provisions of the Atomic Energy Act of 1954 and from the Nuclear Non-proliferation Act of 1978.'

4. The same remark applies to the pyrophoric property of uranium: there appears to be no published study discussing the quantitative importance of this effect in tank warfare.

5. A. Gsponer, J.P. Hurni, and B. Vitale, *A comparison of delayed radiobiological effects of depleted uranium munitions versus fourth generation nuclear weapons*, Report ISRI0207, Proceedings of the 4th Int. Conf. of the Yugoslav Nuclear Society, Belgrade, Sept.30-Oct. 4 2002, Available at: http://arXiv.org/abs/physics/0210071.

6. For the history of their use in anti-tank weapons, see Lanz et al. (2001), Rostker (2000), Davitt (1980), Speer (1970).

7. Moreover, the potential advantage of uranium over tungsten alloys exists only for penetrating metallic targets, not for penetrating concrete or rocks.

8. T.E. Lilios, *Assessing the risk from the depleted uranium weapons used in Operation Allied Force, Science and Global Security* 8 (1999) 163–181.

9. D. Yaziv, M.Mayseless and Y. Reifen, *The penetration process of long rods into thin metallic targets at high obliquity*, 19th International Symposium on Ballistics (7–11 May 2001, Interlaken, Switzerland) 1249–12559. Available at http://www.tsgs.com/.ttk/symp_19/TB261249.pdf.

10. R. Subramanian and S.J. Bless, *Reference correlations for tungsten long rods striking semi-infinite steel targets*, Figure 2, 19th International Symposium on Ballistics (7–11 May 2001, Interlaken, Switzerland) 1249–12559. Available at: http://www.tsgs.com/.ttk/symp_19/TB101115.pdf.

11. B. Rostker, *Development of DU Munitions*, in Environmental Exposure Report, Depleted Uranium in the Gulf (II), (2000). Available at: http://www.gulflink.osd.mil/du_ii/du_ii_tabe.htm. (Curiously, in this section of the extremely well documented 'Gulf Link' website, the comparison of depleted uranium versus tungsten munitions is almost exclusively based on excerpts from a single document, Davitt (1980), which is a relatively old historical review, at a time when much more informative unclassified documents were long since readily available, e.g. Magness and Farrand (1990) and Pengelley (1994)).

12. See, for example Davitt (1980).

13. For example Proceedings of the 1990 Army Science Conference (Durham, NC, May 1990), International Defence Review and the 19th International Symposium on Ballistics (7–11 May 2001, Interlaken, Switzerland).

14. S.P. Andrew, R.D. Caliguri, and L.E. Eiselstein, *Relationship between dynamic properties and penetration mechanisms of tungsten and depleted uranium penetrators*, 13th International Symposium on Ballistics (Stockholm, Sweden, 1–3 June, 1992).

15. R.J. Dowding, *Materials for kinetic energy penetrators*, text of transparencies for a briefing at the Structural Amorphous Metals PreProposal Conference, p4, (Arlington, VA, June 6, 2000). Available at: html at: http://www.darpa.mil/dso/textonly/thrust/md/sam/presentations/dowding.htm.

16. See, for example, J.B. Stevens, *Finite Element Analysis of Adiabatic Shear Bands in Impact and Penetration Problems*, MA thesis (Virginia Polytechnic Institute and State University, 1996). Available at: http://scholar.lib.vt.edu/theses/public/ etd-3753128097370/stevens.pdf.

17. J.B. Stevens and R.C. Batra, *Adiabatic shear banding in axisymmetric impact and penetration problems* (1996). Plots and computer animations available in html at http://www.sv.vt.edu/research/batra-stevens/pent.html.

18. See also L. Magness, L.Kecskes, M.Chung, D. Kapoor, F. Biancianello, and S. Ridder, *Behavior and performance of amorphous and nanocrystalline*

metals in ballistic impacts, 19th International Symposium on Ballistics (7–11 May 2001, Interlaken, Switzerland) 1183–1189. Available at: http://www.tsgs.com/.ttk/symp_19/TB181183.pdf.

19. For instance *Tungsten Heavy Alloy for Anti-tank Ammunition* (Korean Agency for Defence Development, 2001), D.S. Kim et al., *Mechanics of Materials* (1998) and Hong et al *Matrix pools in a partially mechanically alloyed tungsten heavy alloy for localized shear deformation* (2002).

20. See Dowding (2000) and Stevens and Batra (1998).

21. But also Israel, China, Switzerland, Italy, Sweden, Spain, etc.

22. Like most metals (e.g., lithium, aluminum, thorium, etc.), uranium 'burns' (i.e., reacts violently with oxygen) under certain conditions. Usually, uranium is described as a 'combustible metal,' meaning that it burns under appropriate conditions, but without producing the fierce fires that would make it a material of choice for use in incendiary weapons. Uranium is also pyrophoric, meaning that it may ignite spontaneously, which is what happens in air at ambient temperature if it is in powder form. When a uranium projectile impacts on armour, its surface is instantly brought to a temperature of about 3000 degrees, so that any particle that is spalled off, or the remainder of the penetrator, burn until their temperatures fall below a critical temperature. It is estimated that about 20% of a 300 gram 'armour-piercing incendiary (API)' projectile shot by an A10 aircraft is burnt under such conditions. If one assumes that the dominant oxidation process is the $U + O_2 = UO_2$ reaction, the amount of energy set free is 270 kilojoules per mole, which corresponds to the combustion of about 6 grams of napalm. This energy is of the same order as the kinetic energy of the penetrator so that the pyrophoric effect of uranium does not greatly increase the total energy dissipated in the target. Therefore, if a small amount (i.e., a few tens of grams, or a few cubic centimeters) of a highly effective metallic incendiary compound such as 'thermit' were delivered within a hollowed tungsten projectile, or in a follow-through capsule, a much larger incendiary effect would be obtained than with a uranium penetrator of equal weight. (Jean Pierre Hurni, private communication, 20 January 2003).

23. Concurrent Technologies Corporation (2001). Information available at: http://www.ctc.com/index.cfm/fuseaction=1323.

24. The IAEA Safeguards System of 1965-68, IAEA document INFCIRC/66/Rev.2 (IAEA, Vienna, 1968).

25. R. Stone, Belgrade Lab Sets New Course After Top-Secret Uranium Grab, Science 297 (30 August 2002) 1456.

26. Such as the 1971 Atomic Energy Commission initiated rule permitting the commercial use of depleted uranium (See proposed amendment at Federal Register 40, No. 7, January 10, 1975, 2209–2211) and the U.S. International Security and Development Cooperative Act of 1980.

27. Guidelines for Nuclear Transfers, Annex A (Revised 1977 London Guidelines), IAEA document INFCIRC/254/Rev.1/Part 1/Mod. 2 (IAEA, Vienna, April 1994).

28. Ibid.
29. US International Security and Development Cooperative Act of 1980.
30. See, for instance H. Beach, *The military hazards of depleted uranium*, Briefing paper No.78 (International Security Information Service, London, January 2001). Available at:
http://www.isisuk.demon.co.uk/0811/isis/uk/regpapers/no78_paper.html.
31. Dr Lewis Moonie MP, letter to Dr Kim Howells MP about the legality of Depleted Uranium (DU) weapons. Reference D/US of S/LM 1136/01/M (25 March 2001). Excerpt and commentary available at:
http://www.russfound.org/Launch/farebrother2.htm.
32. For an extensive discussion and a comprehensive bibliography see Gsponer and Hurni (2000).
33. For example, the care that is taken in all published documents to avoid any open discussion of the long-term radiological impact of pure fusion nuclear weapons. In fact this impact is very simple to calculate, and immediately suggests a comparison with low radioactive contamination such as that arising from the combat use of depleted uranium.
34. Here, 'military planners' refers not so much to the high ranking soldiers who planned the operations in Iraq or Yugoslavia (or those who previously approved the introduction of depleted uranium weapons into arsenals) but rather to the analysts in defence departments and laboratories, as well as in military think tanks and universities, who shape general policies according to both technical and political considerations, either by direct input to the decision makers, or by omission.
35. The Economics of Tungsten, Roskill reports on metal and minerals, 7th edition, (February 2001). Summary available at:
http://www.roskill.co.uk/tungsten.html
36. See for instance A. Gsponer, *La bombe à neutrons*, La Recherche 15 (No.158, September 1984) 1128–1138 and J. Harris and A. Gsponer, *Armour diffuses the neutron bomb*, New Scientist (13 March 1986) 44–47.
37. S. Sahin and A. Gsponer, *Protection factors of modern armoured tanks against enhanced radiation and fission nuclear warheads*, Atomkernenergie –Kerntechnik 46 (1985) 278–284.
38. The main reason given by these countries has always been that it is contradictory to impose almost zero level release of radioactivity to the environment by the nuclear industry, while at the same time to accept its uncontrolled release by the military.
39. See Rostker (2000).

References

S.P. Andrew, R.D. Caliguri, and L.E. Eiselstein, *Relationship between dynamic properties and penetration mechanisms of tungsten and depleted uranium penetrators*, 13th International Symposium on Ballistics (Stockholm, Sweden, 1–3 June, 1992) 249–256.

H. Beach, *The military hazards of depleted uranium*, Briefing paper No.78 (International Security Information Service, London, January 2001). Available at: http://www.isisuk.demon.co.uk/0811/isis/uk/regpapers/no78_paper.html

Concurrent Technologies Corporation (2001). Information available at: http://www.ctc.com/index.cfm?fuseaction=1323

R.P. Davitt, *A comparison of the advantages and disadvantages of depleted uranium and tungsten alloys as penetrator materials*, Tank Ammo Section, Report No. 107 (U.S. Army Armament Research and Development Command, Dover, NJ, June 1980) Confidential. Pages 3 and 4 at: http://www.gulflink.osd.mil/du_ii/du_ii_tabe.htm

R.J. Dowding, *Materials for kinetic energy penetrators*, text of transparencies for a briefing at the Structural Amorphous Metals PreProposal Conference (Arlington, VA, June 6, 2000). Available at: http://www.darpa.mil/dso/textonly/thrust/md/sam/presentations/dowding.htm

T. Farrand, L.Magness, and M.Burkins, *Definition and uses of RHA equivalences for medium caliber targets*, 19th International Symposium on Ballistics (7–11 May 2001, Interlaken, Switzerland) 1159–1165. Available at: http://www.tsgs.com/.ttk/symp_19/TB151159.pdf

A. Gsponer, *La bombe à neutrons*, La Recherche 15, No.158, Septembre 1984: 1128–1138.

A. Gsponer, J.P. Hurni and S. Klement, *UN security council resolutions 687, 707 and 715 and their implications for a halt of all proliferation prone nuclear activities – a technical and legal assessment*, Report ISRI9606, submitted to Security Dialogue (12 February 1997). Available at: http://nuketesting.enviroweb.org/hew/Iraq/andre/ ISRI-06-06.pdf

A. Gsponer and J.P. Hurni, *The Physical Principles of Thermonuclear   Explosives, Inertial Confinement Fusion, and the Quest for Fourth Generation   Nuclear Weapons*, INESAP Technical Report No.1, Presented at the 1997 INESAP Conference, Shanghai, China, 810 September 1997, Seventh edition, September 2000, ISBN: 3933307102X . Abstract available at: http://nuketesting.enviroweb.org/hew/News/AnnounceReviews.html .

A. Gsponer, J.P. Hurni, and B. Vitale, *A comparison of delayed radiobiological effects of depleted uranium munitions versus fourth generation nuclear weapons*, Report ISRI0207, Proceedings of the 4th Int. Conf. of the Yugoslav Nuclear Society, Belgrade, Sep. 30-Oct. 4, 2002. Available at: http://arXiv.org/abs/physics/0210071

A. Gsponer, *Nanotechnology and fourth generation nuclear weapons*, Disarmament Diplomacy, No. 67 (October/November 2002) 3–6. Available at: http://www.acronym.org.uk/dd/dd67/67op1.htm

J. Harris and A. Gsponer, *Armour diffuses the neutron bomb*, New Scientist, 13 March 1986, 44–47.

Soon H. Hong, Ho J. Ryu, and Woon H. Baek, *Matrix pools in a partially mechanically alloyed tungsten heavy alloy for localized shear deformation*, Materials

Science and Engineering A333, 2002, 187–192. Available at: http://composite.kaist.ac.kr/public/PE56.pdf

The IAEA Safeguards System of 196568, IAEA document INFCIRC/66/Rev.2 (IAEA, Vienna, 1968).

Guidelines for Nuclear Transfers (Revised 1977 London Guidelines), IAEA document INFCIRC/254/Rev.1/Part 1/Mod. 2 (IAEA, Vienna, April 1994).

D.S. Kim, S. Nemat Nasser, J.B. Isaacs, and D. Lischer, *Adiabatic shearband in WHA in high strain rate compression*, Mechanics of Materials 28, 1998, 227–236. Available at: http://www-ceam.ucsd.edu/asia/polycrystal/adiabaticshearband.pdf

Korean Agency for Defense, *Development Tungsten Heavy Alloy for AntiTank Ammunition*, 2001. Available at: http://www.add.re.kr/eng/skill/1.asp

W. Lanz, W. Odermatt, Dr. G. Weihrauch, *Kinetic energy projectiles: development history, state of the art, trends*, 19th International Symposium on Ballistics (7–11 May 2001, Interlaken, Switzerland) 1191–1197. Available at: http://www.tsgs.com/.ttk/symp_19/TB191191.pdf

T.E. Lilios, *Assessing the risk from the depleted uranium weapons used in Operation Allied force*, Science and Global Security 8, 1999, 163–181.

L.S. Magness, and T. G. Farrand, *Deformation behavior and its relationship to the penetration performance of high density kinetic energy penetrator materials*, Proceedings of the 1990 Army Science Conference (Durham, NC, May 1990) 465–479.

L. Magness, L.Kecskes, M.Chung, D. Kapoor, F. Biancianello, and S. Ridder, *Behavior and performance of amorphous and nanocrystalline metals in ballistic impacts*, 19th International Symposium on Ballistics (7–11 May 2001, Interlaken, Switzerland) 1183–1189. Available at http://www.tsgs.com/.ttk/symp_19/TB181183.pdf

Dr Lewis Moonie MP, letter to Dr Kim Howells MP about the legality of Depleted Uranium (DU) weapons. Reference D/US of S/LM 1136/01/M (25 March 2001). Excerpt and commentary available at: http://www.russfound.org/Launch/farebrother2.htm

R. Pengelley, *Tank ammunition development less spectacular, but smarter*, International Defense Review, No. 4/1994 (April 1994) 39–46.

B. Rostker, *Development of DU Munitions*, in Environmental Exposure Report, Depleted Uranium in the Gulf (II), (2000). Available at: http://www.gulflink.osd.mil/du_ii/du_ii_tabe.htm

B. Rostker, *The Economics of Tungsten*, 7th edition, 2001. Summary available at: http://www.roskill.co.uk/tungsten.html

S. Sahin and A. Gsponer, *Protection factors of modern armored tanks against enhanced radiation and fission nuclear warheads*, Atomkernenergie – Kerntechnik 46, 1985, 278–284.

Albert Speer, *Inside the Third Reich*, MacMillan, New York, 1970.

B. Stevens, *Finite Element Analysis of Adiabatic Shear Bands in Impact and Penetration Problems*, MA thesis (Virginia Polytechnic Institute and State University, 1996) . Available at:
http://scholar.lib.vt.edu/theses/public/etd-3753128097370/stevens.pdf

J.B. Stevens and R.C. Batra, *Adiabatic shear banding in axisymmetric impact and penetration problems*, 1996b. Plots and computer animations available at http://www.sv.vt.edu/research/batra-stevens/pent.html .

J.B. Stevens and R.C. Batra, *Adiabatic shear bands in the Taylor impact test for a WHA rod*, International Journal of Plasticity 14, 1998, 841–854. Available at: http://www.esm.vt.edu/¯rbatra/pdfpapers/plasticity1998(841-854).pdf

R. Stone, *Belgrade Lab Sets New Course After Top Secret Uranium Grab*, Science 297 (30 August 2002) 1456.

R. Subramanian and S.J. Bless, *Reference correlations for tungsten long rods striking semiinfinite steel targets*, 19th International Symposium on Ballistics (7–11 May 2001, Interlaken, Switzerland) 1249–12559. Available at: http://www.tsgs.com/.ttk/symp_19/TB101115.pdf

D. Yaziv, M.Mayseless and Y. Reifen, *The penetration process of long rods into thin metallic targets at high obliquity*, 19th International Symposium on Ballistics (7–11May 2001, Interlaken, Switzerland) 1249–12559. Available at: http://www.tsgs.com/.ttk/symp_19/TB261249.pdf

CAMPAIGN AGAINST DEPLETED URANIUM

Affiliate to CADU – the Campaign Against Depleted Uranium

To affiliate, complete this form and send it to us with some money.

I would like to affiliate/be a supporting subscriber (delete as appropriate) to CADU

Name:_____

Address:_____

_____

The affiliation rates (including 1 copy of CADU News quarterly) are:
6 UK pounds for individuals per year; 22 UK pounds for groups per year

Supporting subscribers choose the amount they want to donate, from 2 UK pounds a month upwards

*I enclose a cheque for _____ UK pounds for yearly affiliation

Or, I have filled in the standing order form below for my yearly affiliation (it is much easier for CADU if affiliators could pay by standing order, just enter 6 UK pounds or 22 UK pounds below)

Or, I wish to become a supporting subscriber and have filled in the standing order form below

Account Name:_____

Account Number:_____

Bank Name:_____

Sort Code:_____

Bank Address:_____

_____

I authorise the payment of _____ UK pounds every month / year (delete as appropriate) starting from ____/____/____ (enter date), until further notice, to 'Campaign Against Depleted Uranium', (bank sort code 08-92-99, Account number 65042867) The Co-operative Bank, Kings Valley Yew St, Stockport, Cheshire SK4 2JU

Signed:

Date: ____/____/____

Please fax to +44 (0)161 273 8293 or print and return by post to CADU, Bridge 5 Mill, 22a Beswick Street, Ancoats, Manchester, M4 7HR, UK